BUILDING THE TRIREME

'Then on and on, with ships for spears, they fought'

AESCHYLUS, *The Persians*

BUILDING THE TRIREME

FRANK WELSH

Constable   London

First published in Great Britain 1988
by Constable and Company Limited
10 Orange Street London WC2H 7EG

British Library CIP data
Welsh, Frank
  Building a trireme.
  1. Triremes   2. Ships–Reconstruction
  I. Title
  623.8′21   VM75

ISBN 0 0 09 466880 9

Set in Monophoto Apollo 11pt
and printed in Great Britain by
BAS Printers Ltd, Over Wallop Hampshire

*This account of the latest episode
in the long running Anglo-Hellenic love affair
is dedicated to
all our Greek friends
whose generous co-operation
made the venture possible, and
whose warm friendship made it
always pleasurable.*

CONTENTS

Illustrations

(*Photos of the trireme which are unattributed were taken by the author*)

ACKNOWLEDGEMENTS

Although the design and building of the first sea-going trireme of modern times was primarily due to the remarkable and dedicated work of John Morrison and John Coates, the project could never have been completed without the enthusiastic co-operation of hundreds of others. Some of these are mentioned in the book, but among those many others who are not, and to whom our gratitude is particularly due, are Shirley Kosta, John Jones, Rudi Roth, John Rawson, Anthony Sanctuary, Liz Julien, Len Tipper, Peter Coni, Peter Green and Julie Jones. I am especially grateful to photographers John Ilsley, Dr Liz Carmichael, and my daughter Jane; to John Coates, Jonothan Potter and Owain Roberts for their drawings; and to Graeme Fife for the oarsmen's view on page 220.

The Coates and Morrison families have put up uncomplainingly over the last five years with the pre-occupation of the two Johns. The Randolphs, Rob, Bridie and Claerwen, have shown exemplary patience in the frequent absences and abstractions of their wife and mother, Rosie.

Among the Greek workers and advisers who made notable contributions are Yannis Vrettos, Elias Fragos, Pannayanis Michaelpoulos, Kuriaios Kasdaglis, Dimitrios Yannoudoukas, Evangilous Hadjinkolaus, Nikolous Hadjiyannis and Nikitas Kechagidglou. Admiral Papas, Commodore Isaias and Commodore Vacopoulos of the Hellenic Navy gave constant support.

The always efficient and charming reception staff of the Savoy Hotel, Piraeus, led by Maria; Takis and Stathis Alexopoulos of Greek Island Tours in Poros; and the staff of Saronic Gulf Tours, all made our life in Greece much more agreeable. Prudence Fay proved that rare phenomenon, an editor at once soothing and efficient. Corinne Duhig of the Department of Physical Anthropology at Cambridge led me to the skeletons: Yannis Manuelides reminded me of the piece in Aristotle's *Politics*. John Mitchell designed the book and re-drew many of the diagrams.

F.W.
1987

FOREWORD

Frank Welsh is the 'onlie begetter' of the trireme enterprise. It began as a crazy idea aired by him at a dinner party in the Lake District in May 1982. Five years later the crazy idea became a reality when the trireme replica, designed by John Coates and built at the expense of the Greek government and private Greek benefactors, was launched at Piraeus on 26 August 1987, in front of his eyes. He is, therefore, best placed to chronicle the extraordinary success story of those years.

As a professional writer, and with the perspective of an observer rather than the close involvement that John Coates and I had, he has told the story with verve and imagination – qualities proper in a writer but highly suspect in a historian and still more so in a naval architect. Perhaps the most remarkable thing about the story is not that the replica has been built at all, let alone launched and pulled, but that so many people and institutions gave the enterprise their enthusiastic support in the form of encouragement, ideas, time or money. Among the individual people were the devoted band of oarsmen and oarswomen who paid for their own transport to Greece for the privilege of pulling the trireme; the volunteer team of management who gave up their summer holidays; a housewife from Watlington near Oxford; GPS; staff from the police college at Ryton, and from universities as far apart as Newcastle-upon-Tyne, Bangor and Perth, Australia. Institutions which helped us include the National Maritime Museum at Greenwich; the Hellenic League; and some colleges and the Classical Faculty at Cambridge. Frank Welsh's perceptive and fascinating story makes clear that it was support of this kind that kept up the momentum and succeeded in turning the enterprise from an idea to a reality – a reality which throws a great deal of light on a much-disputed historical conundrum.

This book complements in an attractive way, but does not duplicate, *The Athenian Trireme* by John Coates and myself, published by CUP in 1986.

JOHN MORRISON
1987

The sea-fight off Salamis

Aт midnight on the night of 17/18 September 480 BC the navy of Xerxes, Great King of the Medes and Persians, Lord of Syria, Chorasmia, India, Eygpt, Parthia, Bactria, Lydia, Ionia, and many other satrapies, left its moorings in the harbour of Faliron. One thousand triremes – the latest form of warship, fast oared galleys with crews of more than 200 men, ship-killers that were armed with great bronze rams capable of smashing through enemy timbers in one shattering blow – pulled round the peninsula of Piraeus towards the island of Salamis.

At the same time, in a carefully organized combined operation, a division of the Great King's army, 30,000 strong, lined the northern shores of the bay and ferried a strong detachment of troops to occupy the island of Psyttaleia. The task of these soldiers was to finish off the thousands of Greek seamen who might struggle ashore from their wrecked ships. There were to be no prisoners taken in the battle that was planned, for the objective of the Great King was the final destruction of the impertinent Athenians and their allies.

Not that much remained to be done, for all that survived of Athens was the smoking ruins of the city, the destroyed Acropolis occupied only by the bodies of its defenders. All the other Athenians had fled to take refuge on the island of Salamis or on the coast of Troezen, behind the natural defensive lines of Corinth. They had only just been in time, for Xerxes' cavalry had reached the deserted streets of Athens on 27 August, a mere twenty-four hours after the last inhabitants had left. All Attica had been abandoned to the Persian invaders, and the only Greeks remaining in arms were on board their ships in the harbour of Salamis.

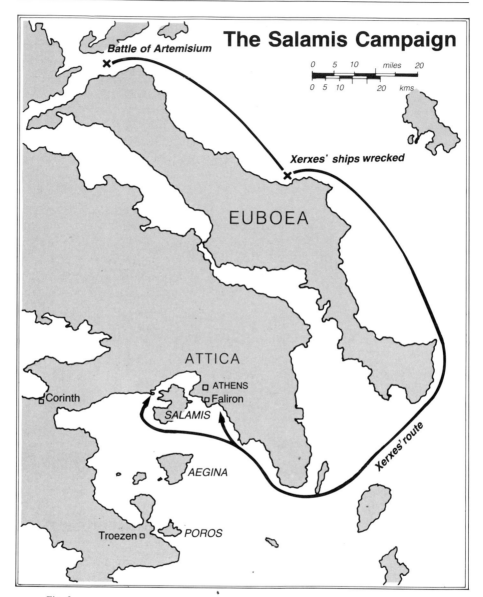

The Salamis Campaign

Battle of Artemisium

0   5   10   miles   20

0   5   10   20   kms

Xerxes' ships wrecked

EUBOEA

ATTICA

Corinth

ATHENS

Faliron

SALAMIS

AEGINA

Xerxes' route

Troezen

POROS

Fig. 1

Xerxes' advance had been irresistible, cutting down through Thessaly and brushing aside the Spartans at Thermopylae. All that now remained for them to do was to destroy the survivors. It was to be the culmination of the greatest campaign the world had ever seen, when the last remaining resistance to the Persian Empire would be permanently obliterated.

There was no doubt in Xerxes' mind as to the outcome of the fight. He made arrangements for a throne to be erected on the shore, at a convenient height to view the battle, and for his secretaries to be in attendance to record the action, so that the courageous might be rewarded and the unsuccessful punished.

If Xerxes was confident, the Greeks had very considerable misgivings. For three weeks they had been lying off Salamis, wondering what to do next and waiting for the Persians to make a move. This must come soon, for the end of the campaigning season was approaching with the advance of autumn. When dawn on the 18th disclosed a huge Persian fleet, far outnumbering their own, lying off Piraeus, it was apparent that the crisis was approaching. They could see the Persian army occupying the shore and the island. The outlook for the Greeks seemed desperate: the gods had already been appealed to; their images had been brought, at some inconvenience, to the fleet, but their efficacy was not universally acknowledged. The Greek commanders remained divided among themselves and spent the whole day vociferously arguing about what should be done.

Many maintained that the only prudent course of action was to retire behind Corinth, where the narrow neck of land formed an impregnable barrier (fig. 1). Not unnaturally this plan had the hearty backing of those whose homes lay behind that line, including Adeimantus the Corinthian and Eurybiades the Spartan admiral. The Athenians, they said, had already lost their country, so what right had they to argue against others who wanted to defend their own?

Themistocles, the leader of the Athenians and the moving spirit behind the resistance to the Persians, firmly pointed out that he had 180 fully armed ships behind him, nearly half the total fleet; with such a force he might choose a new country anywhere he pleased. A hint was dropped that 'anywhere' did not exclude, for example, Corinth. Even should the Athenians choose to go further afield, there was nothing now to prevent them dropping immediately out of the fight, leaving the others to manage as best they could.

The arguments stopped when two ships slipped through the Persian lines with the news that there was now no possibility of retreat or escape.

Xerxes had despatched a powerful squadron round the other coast of Salamis, confining the Greek fleet within the Bay of Eleusis: a battle was inevitable. This was just what Themistocles wanted. He alone of the captains saw quite clearly that if the Persian fleet was destroyed their army would have to withdraw; if the fleet was left intact any idea of defence on land by the Greeks was an illusion. Given command of the seas the Persians could merely bypass the Corinthian fortifications and land their army wherever they pleased behind the lines, picking off the Greek cities one by one. In order to make quite sure that the Great King attacked immediately, Themistocles, who was cunning as well as farsighted, despatched his children's tutor, the slave Sicinnus, to visit Xerxes secretly. Sicinnus, who spoke Persian, gained access to the Great King and told him that the Greeks could not agree among themselves and that they were planning to slip through the Persian blockade that very night. If it did come to a fight there was every prospect that many, especially among the Athenians, would desert to the Persian side.

Whether this completely untrue story played any part in the Great King's decision or not, Xerxes ordered the noose to be drawn tight. At midnight on the 19th, in absolute silence, the Persian fleet moved into the channel. They kept strictly on station, alert to catch the Greeks they thought would attempt to steal through their lines. Of course the Greeks did not try. Daybreak disclosed an unbroken mass of Persian triremes stretching from Salamis to Psyttaleia, and from Psyttaleia to the coast, where the Persian army stood waiting. In spite of having been awake all night, the Persians were the first to move: their leading ships pulled out into the Salamis channel – and into trouble (fig. 2).

Unlike the sites of land battles, those of the sea do not greatly change over the years. The field of Marathon is now flanked by hotels and villas, but the waters of Salamis are still recognizable as those where the battle took place. The strait between Salamis and the mainland narrows to about 1,300 yards. Triremes under oar, if they could keep an absolutely clear course, disregarding any hidden dangers and continuing in a straight line at a uniform speed, in a dead calm, needed about 20 yards of water each. Even given these impossibly favourable conditions it is hard to see how more than seventy or so could have hoped to row in line abreast up the channel.

And there was no dead calm on that equinoctial day, but a lively breeze from the south-west which gave a beam wind, kicking up a chop, and affect-

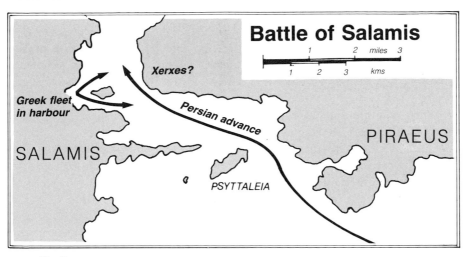

Fig. 2

ing the steering by acting on the tophamper of the Persian ships. Their captains would have found manœuvring impossible, and must have been much
more concerned to pick their way ahead and avoid the ships around them
than to undertake any aggressive action.

Unlike the Persians who had spent the night in their ships without
sleep, keeping station, the Greeks had lain comfortably ashore on the beach
of Paloukia Bay behind St George's Island, screened from the advancing
Persians. They were first heard shouting the war-cry (the paean) even before
the Persians could see them; then in two lines they emerged from either
side of the island.

Aminias of Pallene, commander of an Athenian ship, was the first to
encounter the enemy. It is convenient but inaccurate to talk of Persians
and Greeks. The Greek fleet was certainly all Greek: the biggest contingent
was from Athens, but there were also substantial contributions from Aegina,
Megara, Corinth, Chalcis, Sparta and other cities. But on the other side,
native Persians were not seafarers, and Xerxes' fleet was drawn from his
satrapies – Phoenicia, Eygpt, Cyprus, and from the Greeks of Asia Minor,
whose ships numbered about one-third of the total.

The most prominent vessel in the Persian fleet was the Phoenician flag-
ship commanded by Ariabignes. Loftier and more heavily armed than any
other, she discharged javelins and arrows 'as though from the walls of a

fortress'. Aminias made straight for her. Increasing his striking rate to ramming speed, he sliced into the Phoenician, smashing off her stern. He was followed by the rest of the Athenians, who cut through the solid masses of the Persian fleet. At the same time the other Greek column, racing forward off the island, hit the Persians in their left wing. Their fleet was thus cut in three.

The technique of trireme fighting depended entirely on speed and manœuvrability. The trireme was designed for one end: to disable enemy ships. Her weapon was a triple-edged bronze ram reinforced by a stout oak frame that carried back into the hull. The whole formed a giant spear concentrated on a metal point, fifty tons in weight and capable of speeds of over ten knots. It could tear apart the timbers of any ship it struck.

The blow had to be struck glancingly; a head-on collision at a final speed of something like 30 m.p.h. would be fatal to both ships, while an attack that left the ram embedded would incapacitate the attacker as much as the victim. The ram needed to tear through oars and hull before sliding off freely.

In order to be able to do this, and to avoid being rammed oneself, speed and agility were essential. A ship packed in a close mass and more concerned with avoiding its neighbours, as were the Persians, was at a disadvantage. So too were ships fighting in foreign waters. The Greeks knew the position of shallows and rocks; the Persians had to watch out for these in addition to their other preoccupations.

One of the Greeks fighting that day was a middle-aged poet who had already helped to beat the Persians ten years before at Marathon. Born a few miles away on the mainland, brother to that Aminias who led the battle, Aeschylus was well placed to see what happened, and to write a dramatic, but accurate, account of it in his play *The Persians*. He tells the story as if from the Persian side.

> The whole night long was passed manœuvring,
> Paddling together, keeping to our course,
> Watching for fleeing Greeks who never came.
> Then dawn's white horses touched the distant hills
> And suddenly, appalling, came the noise!
>
> A rhythmic burst of sound came echoing
> From off the island's rocks, crushing our hopes

> For easy and for bloodless victory.
> Those Greeks were bent on fight, not flight . . .
> A Greek ship was the first to charge, and sliced
> The stern clean off from a Phoenician ship.
> Each captain hurled his ship against another.

One translator, Professor Lewis Campbell, gives the last line as: 'Then on and on, with ships for spears, they fought', which gives a vivid idea of the triremes that were described by one later scholar as 'giant arrows'.

> At first we Persians seemed to hold our own,
> But when our ships got well into the strait
> They jammed together, smashing oars on oars,
> Crushing each other with their bronze-clad rams.
> Skilfully dashing in, and striking hard,
> The Greeks soon changed the surface of that sea
> Into a single mess of flesh and wrecks,
> With bodies washed on every beach and shore.

After the Greek columns had broken the Persian line, they were able, as was Collingwood at Trafalgar, to deal with an enemy effectively reduced in force. The Persian fleet turned and retreated as best it might, hotly pursued by the Athenians and the Aeginians, the other Greeks seeming to have had enough.

> Those who could, escaped, but the rest floundered
> Like tunnies gasping in the nets, bludgeoned
> And slashed by Greeks with anything that came
> To hand – broken oars or bits of wreckage.
> Only nightfall brought an end to useless
> Screams and pleas for life . . .

It was a crowded and confused battle, but some incidents were recorded. One ship from Samothrace, fighting for the Persians, sank an Athenian trireme, and was in turn rammed by a ship from Aegina. But the Samothracian javelin men emptied the Aeginian deck and enabled their crew to capture the ship that had sunk them.

One lady, Queen Artemisia of Halicarnassus, distinguished herself.

Before the battle she had warned Xerxes, whose ally she was, against fighting the Greeks on sea, for 'they were to the Persians in a fight as men were to women'. The Great King politely declined her advice, and in the battle itself Artemisia kept her squadron apart until she saw which way the action was going, when she promptly attacked a Persian ship.

Quite unfairly, she got credit for this female trick from both sides; the Greeks believed that she had always intended to help them while Xerxes was misled into thinking it was really a Greek ship she had destroyed.

Xerxes, undoubtedly, had had enough. Two hundred Persian ships had been sunk before his eyes. Their crews had been lost; very few of the Persians were able to swim, and those who struggled to a shore held by the Greeks were immediately killed. Including the garrison of Psyttaleia, about 50,000 Persians must have been slain. Among the dead was Xerxes' own brother.

> Before night fell some Greeks had left their oars,
> Put on their armour, and then leaped ashore.
> Pinning our men down under heavy fire
> Of stones and arrows, they moved right in close.
> The hacking and the stabbing did not stop
> Till every noble Persian there was dead.

Xerxes' advisers, anxious that the royal face should appear to be saved, pointed out that the fight at Salamis was merely incidental. The prime objective of the expedition had been to destroy Athens, and there it was, smoking in ruins behind him. Surely now he could retire with dignity to more pressing concerns elsewhere in his great Empire? And, after all, no real Persian had been beaten, apart from those unlucky ones at Psyttaleia. All the other casualities had been among the lesser breeds, Phoenicians and other native levies. It was all very like Robert Graves' poem:

> 'Truth-loving Persians do not dwell upon,
> That trivial skirmish fought near Marathon . . .'

The Great King, who was nothing if not a realist, saw that this particular game was up. The night after the battle, 21 September, he despatched the nervous remnants of his fleet back to the Dardanelles to secure his retreat to Asia. With naval support withdrawn, the undefeated Persian army took a hiding during its long retreat north. At the battle of Plataea the Persians were smashed; the loot was immense. Xerxes' own kit was captured and the Greek commander was awarded ten of everything taken — women, horses, tents, talents of gold and silver. A tithe of the total was offered to Apollo, in the shape of three golden tripods supported on bronze serpentine pillars. One of these survives in the Hippodrome at Istanbul, and bears the names of those Greek states that fought at Salamis and at Plataea.

The importance of Salamis was well understood at the time, and the battle is unusually well recorded. Aeschylus's eye-witness record apart, Herodotus, in his great history of the Persian Wars, was able to draw upon the accounts of survivors as well as many written records.

We can reconstruct the whole campaign, day by day, in considerable detail. But we know very little of the weapon with which the final battle was fought, the trireme, the ship hurled like a spear against the enemy.

The trireme has been an enigma for centuries. Although superseded both by heavier ships such as quinqueremes, and smaller vessels such as liburnians, triremes continued to serve in Mediterranean navies for hundreds of years, the last being heard of about AD 300. Tens of thousands of these ships must have been built, but no fragment of a single vessel has ever been found.

Classical scholars, archaeologists, ship-designers, and enthusiasts of all persuasions have argued vehemently, for at least the past 400 years, about the real nature of this elusive ship. This book describes how, for the first time, all the known facts were assembled, careful deductions made from them, and the first trireme to be built for 1,500 years was brought again to the waters of the Aegean.

PART I

Fig. 3 Where it all began

1

The great trireme argument

My own interest in the trireme was first aroused over dinner at my house in Westmorland, in April 1982. There were only six of us; Edwin Wolff, a Liverpool solicitor; Charles Willink, classics master at Eton, who has published the first English edition of the *Orestes* to appear this century; and our wives. We were talking over dinner about a correspondence that had recently appeared in *The Times*. The subject had been the Scotch breakfast, and the peculiar custom of eating porridge while standing up. A series of letters had just been crowned by a definitive contribution from another friend, Robert Maxtone Graham, a master of anecdote, whose letters often appear in that newspaper. He had told the story of his grandfather, a Perthshire gentleman who was given to breakfasting every morning wearing a kilt, eating not only porridge walking about his dining-room but also the remainder of the meal. This always included an egg so soft-boiled that he drank it out of the shell to the accompaniment of loud slurping noises, and he completed the meal by peeling an apple with his skean-dhu. The performance, which greatly impressed young Robert, was concluded by his tossing the apple in the air and catching it on the point of the skean-dhu. After that little more could be said on the subject, and the correspondence had duly been closed.

Charles agreed that it was an excellent example of the dottier sort of correspondence which seemed to flourish only in *The Times* and which depended on the willingness of readers to keep up a supply of entertaining stories, and he observed that the longest and not least dotty in the history of that newspaper had taken place a few years earlier on the subject of the trireme.

It is not always easy to define the moment when something starts, but this was unmistakably it. 'Triremes?' Edwin and I said. 'Surely the trireme question has been quite settled; nobody believes any longer in three rows of oarsmen, one above the other?' And we produced the arguments which we had picked up in our schooldays. If a trireme were a three-tiered ship, as might just be feasible, who could fease a quinquereme? Did they really come from distant Ophir? If so, how did they get to Nineveh? Hadn't there been a canal between the Red Sea and the Nile? And anyway Nineveh wasn't a port. Wouldn't a cargo of apes and peacocks have been a nightmare for the crew? Or did the Greeks use slaves? Surely not as fighting men at Salamis? But hadn't Macaulay talked about 'Massillia's triremes, heavy with fair-haired slaves'? And wasn't Marseilles Greek?

It was the first of innumerable similar discussions. Charles attempted to convince us that neither Masefield nor Macaulay could be regarded as sound on triremes, and told us that the matter had been settled, once and for all, by one John Morrison who had been Charles's tutor at Trinity College, Cambridge. Being at that time uninstructed and unregenerate, Edwin and I persisted in our questioning, and looked to the sketchy contents of my library for information. It did not prove very helpful. The most up-to-date work available, the *Oxford Companion to Ships and the Sea* (edited by Peter Kemp) published in 1976, had this to say about triremes:

> Trireme, a war galley of the Mediterranean propelled by three banks of oars. It is generally supposed that the rowers sat on three different levels, a supposition supported by some evidence that the lengths of the oars differed between the 14′ oars pulled by the thranites, rowers in the upper bank, the 10′ 6″ oars pulled by the zygites, rowers in the middle bank, and the 7′ 6″ oars pulled by the thalamites, rowers in the lower bank. Galleys are, however, mentioned in ancient writings with more banks of oars than three, in fact up to seventeen banks, but this cannot refer to banks of oars on different levels, and some other method of classification must have been adopted. It has been suggested that the banks were divided horizontally rather than vertically, and perhaps stepped with the lowest bank aft, a slightly higher bank amidships, and the highest bank in the forward end of the galley.
>
> The trireme was the warship of pre-Christian Greek times. They were armed with a long ram and sometimes carried a few archers and soldiers for boarding. They were credited with a speed of between eight and

Fig. 4 An early nineteenth-century idea of a trireme

nine knots, though only for a short period depending on the strength
and stamina of the rowers.

I was later to discover that the suppositions made in this article were far
from being accurate.

Previous authors, however, seemed to agree with Mr Kemp. The Revd
Edmund Warre, writing in a respectable nineteenth-century edition of the
Encyclopaedia Britannica, set out the three-oar-length theory in some detail.
Seyffert's *Lexicon* (1884) was more cautious. It confirmed the idea of rowers
on three levels, but said: 'The question of the exact arrangement of their
seats, and of the oars, is not yet made out with sufficient clearness.' C. E.
Robinson, in *Everyday Life in Ancient Greece* (OUP) was even vaguer, saying
that it was all 'something of a mystery'.

These references were hardly satisfactory: even to laymen the idea that
a ship could be propelled by oarsmen pulling on three levels with oars so
very different in length sounded peculiar. How could they keep time
together, with one rank pulling on oars longer than those used in a racing
eight, and one using objects not much bigger than a rubber dinghy's
paddles? And how could a ship of considerable size be propelled at any
speed by such insignificant instruments?

Matters got worse when it came to the pictures illustrating these defini-
tions. The best representations showed a tubby but reasonably practicable
vessel (fig. 4). The worst (fig. 5) suggested ships that were certainly picturesque but fanciful in the extreme. None of them could be taken seriously

Fig. 5 A late nineteenth-century idea of a trireme

as a ship capable of being 'hurled like a spear' at the enemy.

Charles was unimpressed, as well he might have been, by the information we had collected. All these sources were misinformed or out of date. For accurate information we must go to John Morrison's definitive work on the subject, in which he insisted that a trireme had three superimposed ranks of oars, and that quinqueremes did not have five ranks but were something altogether other. Continuing dissension was bound to be profitless, but unconvinced and somewhat miffed I said, 'Well, there's only one way to find out, and that's to build one of the things.'

By next morning I had forgotten my indiscretions of the night before when Charles telephoned to say that he thought the idea of building a replica most interesting. Did I mind if he spoke to John Morrison about it? There was little for it but to agree, although not without some trepidation; it was not the first time loose talk over dinner had got me into hot water. But one thing that had better be done quickly was to acquire some further and better information on the subject before encountering so formidable a figure as Professor Morrison, who had not only been Senior Tutor of Trinity, but Head of the Department of Classics and Ancient History in the University of Durham, President of Wolfson College and Senior Tutor and Vice-Master of Churchill College, Cambridge, and Mellon Professor and Kenan Professor in Reed College, Oregon.

The complexity of the problem was borne in on me when I found John Morrison's book *Greek Oared Ships* (with chapters by Roddi Williams and J. R. Blackman; Cambridge University Press, 1968) in the Cambridge University Library. In this substantial work of scholarship Professor Morrison traced hundreds of references to triremes in Greek literature and inscriptions, but in spite of this profusion of written evidence could only offer two fragmentary representations of the ship itself, and even these seemed to be open to question.

Considering that the trireme was for some 800 years the standard warship of the Mediterranean, forming the mainstay of any community with pretensions to naval influence, it seemed amazing that the evidence as to its appearance should be so sparse. Athenians, Lydians, Phocaeans, Spartans, Syracusans, Etruscans, Rhodians, Egyptians, Phoenicians, Carthaginians, Romans, all had fleets of triremes: many thousands must have been built, all large and expensive vessels. Surely there ought to be some surviving pictures of them?

But then, what might some New Zealand archaeologist of the forty-first century, visiting ancient London in order to sketch the ruins of St Paul's from the remaining arch of Westminster Bridge, make of so common an object as the London bus?

> Although we are fortunate at Te Awamutu in having preserved almost intact the entire collection of the National and Tate Galleries, it is surprising and unfortunate that no clear representation of a London bus has survived. Literary allusions must be relied upon to provide the basis of any reconstruction, and these are tantalizingly contradictory. Certainly for some time in the early XIX century right up to the first Nuclear War the omnibus (vulg. bus) was of major importance in the life of everyday Londoners. It is clear from the works of Dickens and Surtees that regular services were provided in the first part of that era, although these appear to have declined both in speed and reliability

by the last quarter of the twentieth century. But the essential questions remain unsolved; was the bus drawn by horses or powered by a primitive engine? Were there, one, two or more levels of passengers? The nature of the mysterious 'trolley' bus is still unknown. Considering what we know the difficulties and privations experienced towards the end of that era we must suppose that as the social fabric disintegrated the more reliable horse supplanted the early engines, a thesis rendered more probable by the reverence with which that now extinct animal was held by the ancestors of our present monarch.

Somewhat surprisingly, earlier ships were better documented. Oared galleys had been used in the Mediterranean for 2,000 years before the trireme put in its appearance, and pictures of Mycenaean ships show a clearly recognizable type, closely resembling later vessels. These had sharply upswept sterns and a projecting forefoot resembling a ram, although this feature was probably a vestige of their origins as dug-out canoes.

Quite possibly this sort of ship survived the invasions that ended Mycenaean civilization, and brought about the Greek Dark Ages (1200–800 BC). Certainly Homer's epics, which were written about 750 BC but which describe events that took place 500 years or so earlier, are full of ships and seafaring, and give a clear idea of what ships of the end of the 2nd millenium BC were like. The Greek ships that were beached off Troy, and that carried Odysseus on his wanderings, were open galleys with all members of the crew taking an oar, using sails as an auxiliary when the wind served. The standard type was a pentecontor, a '50er', the numeral referring to the number of oars. Ships might have fewer oars – triacontors, '30ers', were common, '20ers' were used as despatch vessels, and there is one particular mention of a '60er' – but a '50' was the 'ship of the line'. She was not a fighting vessel *per se*, but a troop transporter carrying exploring or raiding parties very much as Viking ships did 3,000 years later. Like Viking ships, which made extended expeditions, pentecontors could also carry a fair cargo in the hold and were capable, under the right conditions, of voyages of some length.

Many representations of pentecontors survive, dating from as early as 1400 BC. Older drawings, often faithfully depicting the twenty-five oars a side, need some interpretation (fig. 6) before it is clear that they represent almost precisely the same ship as that of 700 years later. The salient features – projecting forefoot, upswept stern, steering oars, brailed square sail – are identical.

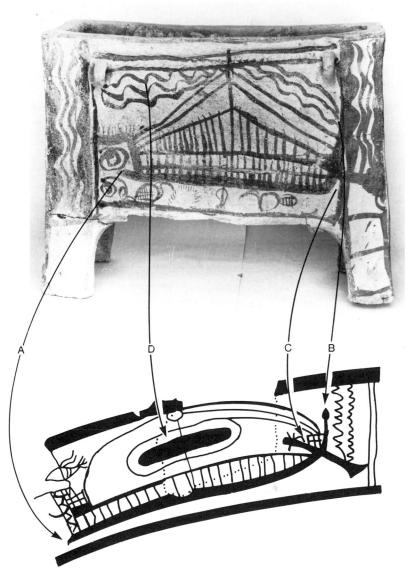

Fig. 6 Mycenean ships
A = projecting forefoot; B = swept-up stern
C = steering oar; D = brailed sails

Fig. 7 Seventh century BC – a one-level warship, pentecontor or smaller

Later, while we were planning our ship, a reconstruction of such a Homeric vessel was taking place. This was the achievement of Tim Severin, who had earlier made successful voyages in reconstructions of a medieval skin boat and an Indian Ocean dhow. His *Argo* was a '20er' although sometimes rowed by as few as eight oarsmen, and in her he retraced the journeys of Jason and of Odysseus. His account of these voyages was published in two handsome books *The Jason Voyage* and *The Ulysses Voyage* (Hutchinson, 1985 and 1987) and a television series was broadcast.

Naturally a good deal of interest was taken in these activities, and we had often to explain how our own project differed.

In the first place Tim was an adventurous seafarer who had started with the idea of retracing historic voyages in replicas of the ships that would orginally have been used. His expedition across the North Atlantic following St Brendan's route in a skin boat is especially likely to remain one of the classics of sailing literature. We, in contrast, were elderly gentlemen who would rely on younger and fitter persons to work the trireme and to try to match the performances recorded in history. We would be content to observe their efforts from a comfortable position on the poop.

Then *Argo* was a good sea-going boat, capable of decent performance under sail in moderately bad weather. She was not an advanced or specialized type but a straightforward open pulling boat, not much different from a modern naval cutter and capable, like her forebears, of carrying cargo and provisions for extended voyages. The trireme, on the other hand, was a specialized and dedicated ship-killer, a guided missile deployed only in the most favourable conditions. She carried no cargo, and provisions enough only for quick trips between supply points. And there had been no real historical controversy as to the way in which *Argo* should be built; enough was known about the nature of the ship and the methods that were used. But the trireme had been the subject of fierce discussion for centuries. Proving the correctness of our theories of oar-arrangement would be only the starting point: many other hypotheses remained to be tested.

Argo's construction was a more straightforward matter. Her hull was sufficiently wide and deep to do without the specialized techniques that the trireme needed, and she was quite capable of being built by a two-man enterprise on a convenient bit of shore (but two men, it should be added, of remarkable quality).

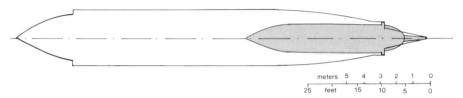

meters 5 4 3 2 1 0
25 feet 15 10 5 0

Fig. 8. Argo *compared in size with the trireme*

And of course the trireme was very much bigger (fig. 8); a crew of 200 rather than a maximum of twenty brought with it problems of an altogether different dimension both in construction and handling. At the time we started, however, all these considerations lay very much in the future.

The history of war at sea only properly began when ships became capable of attacking other ships. Hints of this development in naval warfare first appeared in the seventh century BC, when a painter, Aristonothos, produced a vase which showed two ships of different types, one clearly Greek, the other notably foreign (probably Etruscan), apparently ramming each other. This is possibly the first record of ship-to-ship fighting (fig. 9). Written evidence of such tactics comes a century later when a Phocaean Greek fleet was able, using rams, to defeat an Etruscan fleet twice its size. It seems that the Greeks had discovered a powerful new weapon, which they proceeded to perfect with some speed.

Success with ramming depends upon speed and manœuvrability; both of these qualities may be increased if more manpower can be packed into the hull. A pentecontor was rowed, like a modern cutter, by men sitting

Fig. 9 The Aristonothos vase: a Greek galley with ram (left) attacks an oared warship, probably Etruscan

on the thwarts or cross-benches. If a second tier could be formed by sitting men under the thwarts, in the hold space of the boat, the power available would be doubled. This was done, and from about 600 BC there are pictures of pentecontor types with two levels of oarsmen (fig. 10).

It is tempting to refer to these ships as 'two-deckers', but the temptation should be resisted; like all galleys of the period, two-level pentecontors were large open boats, completely undecked.

All this is clear, well understood and not disputed; abundant representation of two-tiered galleys exists, although irritatingly, nobody apparently gave a separate name to them for several hundred years. The trouble, which has continued to the present day, began when references to *triereis*, 'three-ers', or triremes, whatever they may have been, appeared. (The correct Greek word is *trieres* (pl *triereis*) but the latinized 'trireme' is so commonly used that we have retained it except when used in a specific context.) The historian Thucydides, who himself commanded a trireme in the Peloponnesian War, gave the credit for building the first trireme to the Corinthians, about 650 BC; he added that the 'first sea-fight' a generation later, was also a Corinthian innovation. This clash was presumably between triremes.

The new weapon was an instant success. As soon as states could afford it (or even before they could afford it) fleets were changed from pentecontors (single- or double-tiered) to triremes.

By 500 BC the trireme had completely superseded the pentecontor, as all the states of the Eastern Mediterranean equipped themselves with the first ship-killing ship, the progenitor of all subsequent warships. (The trireme was also the direct inspiration for the first iron-clad battle tactics.

When the use of steam gave ships once more a degree of manœuvrability comparable with that of the trireme, the ram became for a time again an important weapon. For half a century after the battle of Lissa in 1866, when an Italian battleship was sunk by an Austrian ram, ramming was central to naval tactics.)

Some states particularly excelled in the use of the new ship. The Sidonians were regarded as the crack squadron of the Anatolian coast, with Queen Artemisia of Halicarnassus, who commanded her fleet in person, a close second. But the greatest success was that of Athens after Salamis; for 160 years, with some ups and downs, the Athenians enjoyed maritime supremacy. The original trireme was unbeatable when rowed by Athenians; rival powers wishing to go one better had to invent something different. One better was duly gone by the Syracusans in 413, when a fleet of Athenian triremes was totally destroyed by Syracusan ships that had been heavily reinforced, making them slower but more powerful than the light Athenian vessels. From then on, rival naval powers had to build bigger and heavier, replacing the ram with a combination of missile attack and boarding by larger crews. The sequence of events parallels that of the Hundred Years' War, when the French, finding the English long-bow invincible, developed the new artillery arm, enabling the unromantic Bureau brothers to smash the last English army at Castillon.

Syracuse, always a centre of technology (Archimedes was a Syracusan),

Fig. 10 Two-tier pentecontor, sixth century BC

continued to lead developments. At the beginning of the fourth century BC Dionysius of Syracuse built 'fours' and fives' (*tetreres* and *penteres* in Greek; quadriremes and quinqueremes in Latin); his son advanced to 'sixes'. After the death of Alexander the Great quarrels between his generals and their descendants carried the move further. By the end of the century the famous Macedonian Demetrius Poliorcetes (Beseiger of Cities) had 'eights', 'nines', 'tens', 'elevens', 'thirteens', 'fifteens' and one 'sixteen'. Ptolemy of Egypt, descendant of another general of Alexander's capped these with 'twenties' and 'thirties'.

Absolutely the last word in oared ships, a 'forty', was launched by his successor, Ptolemy IV Philopator, towards the end of the third century. This vessel naturally aroused great public interest, and a careful description of it survives. The *tesseraconteres* was 420′ long, with a beam of 47′ and a draught of only 6′: the air draught however was 72′ at the prow and nearly 80′ at the stern. These dimensions would be impossible in a single-hulled ship and indeed the information is added that she was double-prowed and double-sterned. She was therefore presumably double-hulled too; i.e. a catamaran. She carried no fewer than 4,000 oarsmen.

It was this profusion of digits that gave rise to the subsequent confusion as to the nature of the trireme. As Edwin Wolff and I had protested at our first discussion, a two-tiered ship is entirely possible; there are in fact several ancient pictures of such vessels. But an eight-tiered ship? Or the skyscraper that a forty-tiered ship must have represented? Surely quite absurd. (Not that absurdity ever stopped a dedicated triremer. Several attempts (see fig. 11) have been made to show how a 'forty' might have worked.)

In dismissing such manifestly impossible ideas, and in the absence of clear evidence, many writers have also jettisoned the concept of a three tiered trireme. They argue that since the enumerator of a 'forty' clearly applies to something other than the tiers, so equally does that of a trireme. The number might refer to men per oar, or a formula of some other sort, but not to levels or tiers. This argument is strengthened by the fact that nowhere in the world at any other time has there been a ship with three-tiers of oars. Indeed, we have only tracked down one other undoubted type of two-leveller – a Javanese merchant ship of the nineteenth century.

The future New Zealand archaeologist might have a similar difficulty with the London bus:

It seems beyond doubt that buses existed with decks on at least two

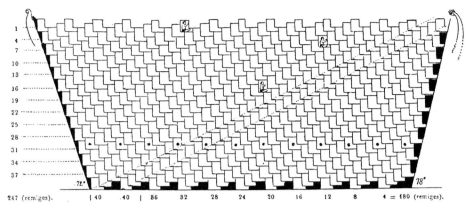

Fig. 11 *A 40-tier ship? A suggested arrangement of men*

levels, and it is therefore odd that no special signifier of the difference appears in the language of the period. There are, by contrast, many references to 'number elevens' and 'seventy-threes': the last are often described by their invariable custom of travelling in groups. It is manifestly unrealistic to suppose that these numerals had reference to the number of decks or levels; even a nine-decker would be unimaginable in the conditions of the time, and a seventy-three-decker is clearly impossible.

Given the proclivity of the age for living according to thousands of minor regulations for which no rational explanation has been proffered, it is most likely that the London bus was graded according to its passenger-carrying capacity. Thus a 'nine' would be the smallest vehicle, capable of carrying only that number of passengers, and possessing a single deck. A 'seventy-three' would have been much larger, and presumably accommodated at least some of its passengers on a secondary deck, doubled alongside the driver as shown in coloured engravings of the 'stage-coach'.

The modern argument about triremes began at the Renaissance, when a renewed interest in classical matters was stimulated by the rediscovery of Greek literature in the West after the fall of Byzantium (1453). At that time large, oared warships were still an everyday presence in the Mediterranean and even in northern waters; familiarity with these coloured the earliest assumptions made. The French humanist Budé, describing a trireme in the early sixteenth century, attributed to it a contemporary Mediterranean oar system: 'ships of three rows of oars are called triremes by our moderns, triereis by the Greeks; in these ships three oarsmen sit to each bench each pulling his own oars, so that the man who sits furthest inboard pulls the longest oar' (the *a zenzile* system). A Venetian mathematician, Vittore Fausto, built what he called a trireme, which appears to have worked, but was probably just such a three-man-to-a-bench ship as Budé described.

Such vessels were a far cry even from Roman triremes, and a world away from the Greeks. The fast, undecked Athenian trireme lasted for less than a century before being superseded by the modified heavier, fully-decked and protected ships introduced by the Syracusans. By the fifth century AD the historian Zosimus had to record that the method of building triremes had long since been forgotten. The three-level oared ship had finally disappeared.

At the time of the Renaissance, although literary evidence was available, archaeological indications were few and far between. The best dated from 500 years after Salamis – the boats shown on Trajan's column in Rome (fig. 12) are clearly biremes and triremes, with oars at two or three levels. Understandably enough, these dubious-looking craft were dismissed by Renaissance commentators in favour of the efficient and well-known galleys that could then be seen in any Mediterranean port.

Some voices were raised in protest at this assumption, among them that of Sir Henry Savile, who, being a sixteenth-century Englishman, was less exposed to these influences. Sir Henry, a distinguished scholar, Provost of Eton, Warden of Merton College, was described as 'the magasine of all learning', and '*ad miraculum eruditus*'. He wrote that the ideas of Budé and the Italians were 'directly against both the authority of ancient writers produced by themselves, and contrary to the ancient portraytures remayning yet to be seene'.

Those who like Sir Henry maintained that the classical trireme had three levels of oars, rather than three men to a bench or to a single oar, faced another difficulty which Edwin and I had spotted: three levels of oarsmen would seem to require oars of three different lengths. We found this hard to swallow. Barras de la Penne who, as captain of Louis XIV's galleys, knew what he was talking about, pointed out in 1727 that oars of different lengths

Fig. 12 The carving on Trajan's column

at different levels could not be rowed in time together, which would be an absolute necessity with so many oarsmen.

There the matter rested until the Enlightenment and the beginnings of methodical archaeology at the beginning of the nineteenth century brought a revival of interest in classical matters. At that time two important new pieces of evidence appeared. The first was a comprehensive list of naval stores held in the Athenian arsenal of the fourth century BC. These inventories, engraved on stone tablets, constitute the best sort of evidence; clear, official and unequivocal. There is no need to edit or deduce theories from such prosaic documents, which do nothing more than list items of stores. Among these were enumerated the oars carried on a trireme: 170 oars were classified as being sixty-two thranite, and fifty-four each zygian and thalamian. Thirty spare oars were provided; these were of two lengths, 9 cubits (3.99 m) and 9.5 cubits (4.2 m).

This particular piece of information proved to be a key to the proper understanding of the trireme, although its significance was not immediately

Fig. 13 The Lenormant relief

appreciated. The slight difference in lengths – eight inches or so – makes it impossible that these spare oars were intended to be used on different levels. The reason must be – and there is other evidence to support this deduction – that the slightly shorter oars would be needed where the hull narrows at either end, restricting the room available to the oarsmen.

The second discovery took the form of a fragment of marble found in the ruins of the Erechtheion in 1859, and named after its discoverer. The Lenormant relief (fig. 13), requires some interpretation in order to understand it as a representation of a three-level galley (fig. 14). The third, topmost tier is rowed from an outrigger (the supports for which can be seen) by oarsmen pulling under the shelter of a canopy deck, with open sides to it. Only the top tier of oarsmen, the thranites, are visible: from the height of their seats it may be concluded that they are sitting at near-gunwale level, some distance above the thwarts. The others are concealed by the hull. Their

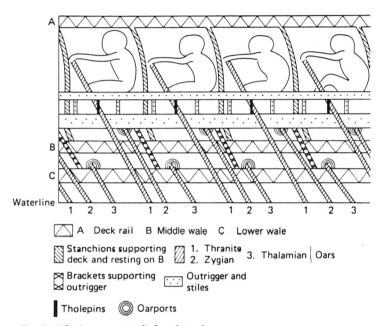

Fig. 14 The Lenormant relief explained

positions can be deduced by following the point where the oars strike the water to that where they enter the hull; there they sit, the zygians on the thwarts, with the thalamians below and behind them, in the belly of the ship. The vertical separation of the levels is nowhere near enough to allow for their sitting directly above each other; if the dimensions are accurate, they must be almost in one another's laps.

These two new pieces of evidence revived the debate, and the first attempt at reconstructing a trireme was begun, inspired by the Emperor of the French, Napoleon III.

Louis Napoleon, in contrast to his blood-thirsty uncle, was a comparatively peaceable and agreeable man. At the apogee of his reign, the Emperor felt inspired to demonstrate his own erudition and to underwrite the Imperial pretensions of his house, which he rightly felt were regarded by foreign royalties as a bit of a joke. He decided to write a biography of Julius Caesar, and as a piece of ingenious sales promotion instructed one Auguste Jal to co-operate with the eminent naval architect Dupuy de Lôme in order to build a trireme.

Jal and de Lôme were, on the face of things, admirably qualified. Auguste Jal was a native of Lyons, a professor of classics, who had made his reputation by publishing in 1838 an enormous prolix and multilingual encyclopaedia of nautical terms. His enthusiasm was boundless, although not always compatible with strict standards of scholarship, or even relevance. In his article on triremes he recollects the triple-hulled trimarans found in the Pacific, and suggests that the adaptation of that principle to the trireme might solve the problem of stability. Jal's illustration of this is one of the more exotic items of trireme lore.

Stanislas Charles Henri Laurent Dupuy de Lôme was more practical, a famous naval architect from an old Breton family in Morbihan. French shipbuilders had always been able to produce magnificent vessels, but de Lôme's masterstroke, the armoured screw frigate *Gloire* built in 1859, revolutionized the concept of warship building. She was the first ocean-going armoured ship, fitted with breech-loading rifled guns and more than a match for any ship then afloat. The British Admiralty was prompted in reply to build the superb *Warrior*, and the race to produce faster and more powerful warships was on. Since then the French navy has always included a capital ship named after Dupuy de Lôme.

The outcome of this, the only other attempt in the last 1,500 years to build a trireme, is of compelling interest to anyone contemplating a second: unfortunately it was totally unsuccessful. Some responsibility for the failure must rest with Napoleon himself, who pressed the project ahead at an impossible speed – the contract for building was signed before plans had been prepared, yet the ship was finished in only seven months. This ruled out any possibility of organized research and development which might have led to better results. After the briefest consultation with Jal, de Lôme went ahead to design a good sea-going galley bearing only the most superficial resemblance to an Athenian trireme (fig. 15), if indeed that is what she was meant to be.

Fig. 15 Louis Napoleon's 'trireme'

The ship was launched in March 1861: she was not named, which might have given a clue as to whether a Greek ship was intended, but was entered in the naval lists as a '*bâtiment speciale*', commanded by Lieutenant Lefebvre. The designers do not in fact seem to have been at all clear as to whether they were attempting to build an Athenian trireme or a much later ship. It was after all a first-century Roman vessel that the Emperor had in mind, but Jal specifically took the Lenormant (Athenian) relief of 300 years earlier as a guide. But whether it was intended to be Greek or Roman, Jal and

43

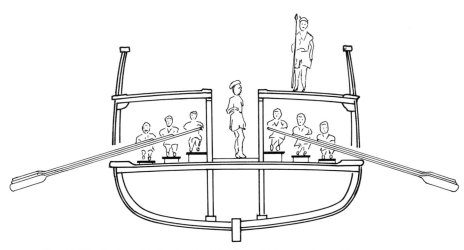

Fig. 16 The U-shaped hull: sketch of Wigham Richardson's model

de Lôme were wrong on a fundamental point. Like the previous Renaissance commentators they thought of the trireme in terms of the ships they themselves knew. The hull of a mid-nineteenth-century ship had a U-section, with a flat bottom and a degree of tumblehome (the sides of the hull sloping in towards the deck). It can be seen from the drawing (fig. 16) that if this sort of shape is used in designing a three-banked rowing ship the oars must inevitably be of very unequal length in each tier. Although the oarsmen would have doubtless been picked men, experienced at pulling heavy boats at sea, their task was herculean. Napoleon's trireme displaced over 100 tons, but was pulled by only 130 oars. (Ours, when the design was complete, was less than half the weight, and had 170 oars.) It is not known why the lower number was chosen: no historic justification exists for it, nor for the unnecessary ornamentation – eagles, crowns, zinc stars, to say nothing of two separate rams, copper sheathing to the hull, and ten tons of ballast.

Jal's thalamians must have had a more than usually confined existence, since they were placed under a completely unhistorical deck and thereby cut off from the upper ranks. This deck also necessitated raising the freeboard (the height of the ship above the waterline), so forcing an increase in the length of the thranite oars.

It was hardly surprising that the Napoleonic trireme failed. She was given only one outing, on the Seine, with the Emperor aboard. This was from the Pont de St Cloud to the Pont de Neuilly and back, a distance of about four miles in each direction. The oarsmen managed 5.5 knots downstream, with a current estimated at about one knot. Even this modest achievement speaks volumes for the skill of Lefebvre's men, although they were doubtless relieved at not being asked to go further.

After this the Emperor seems to have lost interest, and later that summer the trireme was towed to Cherbourg, where she was left to rot. Fourteen years afterwards an unsympathetic republican government agreed to the request of Admiral Cloué that she should be used as a target for torpedo practice. Hardly a fortunate precedent, it might be thought, for anyone rash enough to attempt another reconstruction.

Yet amateurs of trireme design were not dejected by this sad event. A deluge of publications from German, Swedish, Bulgarian, Austrian and Italian savants explored the most eccentric theories: but, wisely, no one ventured on another reconstruction.

Towards the end of the nineteenth century English scholars began to interest themselves in the trireme controversy, which had hitherto been more popular among Europeans. They proved themselves equally original: one Mr Bussey, a naval architect, recognizing that rowers equipped with oars of unequal length could not be expected to pull together at the same time, suggested that the two lowest ranks, with the shortest oars, would have paused between strokes to let the others catch up. A Mr Haweis went further along these lines, claiming that in a quinquereme the two lowest ranks would have made four strokes with their short oars while at the same time the next two ranks made two strokes and the highest rank one – and all while keeping in time!

The most influential of the English commentators was Sir William Woodthorpe Tarn, who made the trireme very much his own subject for nearly half a century. Tarn was a man of parts, a scholar of Eton and Trinity, a lawyer until bad health persuaded him to retire to Scotland, one of the best shots in Britain, a pianist, writer of a once-famous children's story, *The Treasure of the Island of the Mist*, who served on the War Office Intelligence staff during the First World War. In his enforced retirement, Tarn became a distinguished ancient historian, author of a weighty book on Alexander, and a major contributor to the *Cambridge Ancient History*. Like many who are cut off from personal contact with other scholars, Tarn grew opinionated, and intolerant of those whose views differed from his own.

These characteristics showed themselves in his first article on triremes in the *Journal of Hellenic Studies* in 1905. Tarn contemptuously dismissed anyone who disagreed with him. 'Assman's hoch-polyereis theory . . . little relation to the evidence . . . Weber's book, with many blunders and mistranslations . . . However little one wishes to dogmatize, one cannot always be writing in the potential mood . . .'

Tarn was convinced by the numbers argument: if a forty-tier, or even a five-tier, ship was absurd then so was a three-tier trireme. He found literary references that could be interpreted to support this point of view and concluded that 'superposed banks of oars, in the accepted sense, are a practical impossibility'. Support for this view came in the same year from the *Classical Review* where, in an attempt to demonstrate that Tarn's ideas could work, A. B. Cook and Wigham Richardson of the famous Tyneside shipbuilding yard constructed a model (fig. 16) which needed oars of quite different lengths – 3.05 m, 3.65 m, and 4.11 m – had far too low a freeboard to be even modestly seaworthy, and accorded with none of the available evidence.

Tarn was not a man to be excessively bothered by inconvenient facts: where these contracted his theories they were simply ignored. The embarrassing division of the oarsmen into three classes, vouched for in the Athenian navy lists, was fatuously explained by him as meaning not top, middle and bottom, but fore, midships and aft.

Such was Tarn's authority that no voices were raised in protest, and writing twenty-five years later he was able to maintain: 'As I understand the evidence, the trireme question has long been settled on a one-level basis.' But although dogmatic, Tarn was not imperceptive, and in the same article he remarked that previous commentators had misunderstood the essential nature of the trireme.

> When we think of a ship, we are apt to think of something very solid – a liner, a battleship, and so on. A Greek naval fighting machine was anything but solid; and I would ask you for a few minutes to forget all you know about ships and to think of a glorified racing eight . . . a trireme was a comparatively light machine of shallow draught and low freeboard.

A 'glorified racing eight' is by no means a bad description of the early

Athenian triremes. By making this clear statement Tarn dispelled a multitude of misconceptions and cleared the way for a solution to the trireme problem.

But by then the previously universal acceptance of Tarn's views was beginning to erode, and criticisms emerged. They surfaced after an article he wrote in 1933 in the *Mariner's Mirror* ('wherein may be discovered his Art, Craft, and the Mystery after the mariner of their use in all ages and among all nations'), a journal dedicated to the discussion of seafaring history. The article appeared – between one on the Cinque Ports' Feud with Yarmouth in the thirteenth century and another on 'Letters from Sir Samuel Hood 1780–82' – and was entitled 'The Oarage of Greek Warships'. Tarn went at it bald-headed in his usual style.

> I have been asked to write something about the question of how Greek warships were rowed, a question which has long been the Cinderella of classical studies; even today many people believe that they were rowed by superimposed banks of oars. Now it does not matter in the least to anybody how an ancient galley was rowed; but it does matter vitally to every one of us that we should handle evidence, in whatever subject, in the proper way. The laws of mechanics were the same 2,000 years ago as today, and the Greek gods were not in the habit of performing continuous mechanical miracles such as would have been necessary had efficient warships really been rowed by a number of banks of oars one above the other . . .

Dr Tarn – he was knighted only towards the end of his long life – went on stoutly to deny that any archaeological evidence for a three-level trireme existed; though just to be on the safe side he stated that the question was 'principally one for history and philology, not for archaeology'. He was able to do this only by ignoring another piece of evidence, the Ruvo vase (of which more hereafter), and dismissing the Lenormant relief as 'a so-called trireme' describing it as 'really a galley with single one-man oars'.

He ended as blisteringly as he began: 'As to the theory of superimposed banks, its only interest seems to be that it may some day provide an answer to the time-honoured question, "Is an error, once well started, indestructible?"'

Tarn had gone a little too far, and the next issue carried an annoyed note from Dr R. C. Anderson:

Since the responsibility for inviting Dr Tarn to write in the *Mariner's Mirror* on the arrangement of oars and rowers in Greek galleys, was mine, I feel a certain hesitation in disagreeing. Still, as an unconvinced believer in the 'impossible' superimposed arrangement of triremes' oars, I do feel that some of Dr Tarn's views need reconsideration.

Dr Anderson, who was an authority on sailing vessels and who later went on to write a book on oared warships (*Oared Fighting Ships*, Argus Books, 1962), became quite severe, and went on: 'I hardly think that Dr Tarn can have thought out the full implications of his theory . . . the thing simply won't work . . .'

He was given support by H. I. Chappelle: 'Dr Tarn has jumped to a conclusion without careful consideration of the existing evidence.'

The Doctor wasn't taking this lying down, and wrote five pages in reply, leaving his opposition fatigued if not convinced. But by this time a new figure had appeared on the scene. The young John Morrison had taken an interest in the subject, and had begun his work on what should be the eventual solution to this very long-lived problem.

2

A certain amount of ancient evidence

Aɴʏ casting director searching for an actor to take the part of Master of
an Oxbridge college would be delighted to come across John Morrison. Tall,
affable, with an indefinable air of slightly abstracted distinction not
diminished by a degree of sartorial informality, he is one of nature's Heads
of House. John's mild and studious air conceals much tenacity and firmness.
He ended an academic career as first President of Wolfson. It is not easy
to excel as head of a famous college that has been established for centuries;
to do so for a nascent organization beset by problems of fund-raising, working in a clutter of building operations, and making initial appointments that
will enable the college to take its place worthily in a distinguished muster,
is a monstrous task. Having performed it with notable success, and at a
time when most men would be entrenched in retirement, John, a man of
great energy, was immediately ready to start the almost equally difficult
endeavour of presiding over the trireme reconstruction.

   At the time we met, in the early summer of 1982, John had been con-
cerning himself with triremes for nearly half a century. He first encountered
Dr Tarn when, as an undergraduate, John had been making up for time
lost during term by working in the vacation in the London library of the
Hellenic Society. Deep in his studies, he became aware of huffing and puffing
behind him. Being a dedicated student he paid no attention, but immersed
himself in his books. Eventually the librarian came up. 'Excuse me, sir, but
you're sitting in Dr Tarn's chair. Would you mind moving? He's used it
for twenty-five years.'

   On that occasion John gracefully gave way to Dr Tarn, but it was the
last time he was to do so. The outbreak of war gave John, who joined the

Royal Navy, the opportunity to consider the trireme problem and to devise a possible solution. He intended this to be in accordance with the archaeological evidence available, and consonant with all the texts. The results were published in a *Mariner's Mirror* article in 1941. Conscious of the doctor's seniority and his weight in these matters ('the vigorous championship of Dr Tarn'), John advanced his theory less brashly, but equally firmly: it 'rested upon a certain amount of ancient evidence, which the other [Dr Tarn's] did not share'.

John first disposed of the idea which had especially engaged the attention of Italian enthusiasts: that there was a continuity of design between ancient triremes and Venetian galleys. On the contrary, it was quite clear that the Romans had preferred smaller, lighter ships, and that by AD 400, as Zosimus had said, the method of building triremes had been entirely forgotten. An entirely different method of ship construction had developed over the thousand years of the Byzantine empire, which made it impossible that ancient designs had exercised any influence over subsequent oared vessels. Renaissance galleys were the products of a different technology. They were fast gunships, operating under sail as well as oar and intended to provide a mobile platform for heavy artillery pieces, whereas the light Athenian trireme itself constituted the missile.

John's article went on to consider the archaeological evidence which Dr Tarn had chosen to ignore, starting with some evidence that substantiated his own interpretation of the Lenormant relief. As well as another fragment of the original sculpture, a second relief, carved to the same scale, had been discovered in Italy. This shows the first four oarsmen on the port side, starting from stroke, and is particularly useful since it indicates – as might be expected due to the curve of the hull – that there were more rowing positions on the top (thranite) line than on the lower two.

Other related evidence came from a drawing in the British Museum made for a seventeenth-century Italian, the Cavaliero dal Pozzo. This shows something very like the Lenormant relief, but includes the bows, together with an impressive ram (fig. 17). Rams are quite well documented on vases, vase-paintings, coins and monuments, therefore they were clearly as striking to the Greek imagination as to ours. It is true that the dal Pozzo drawing does not indicate the three tiers at all clearly; one can only assume that the Renaissance copyist had made the same mistake that was made by so many others. Since he had never come across anything like a classical trireme, he adapted what he saw to accord with his own conception of an

Fig. 17 The dal Pozzo drawing

oared galley, converting the middle tier of oars into some sort of indeterminate structure like that shown supporting the outrigger.

Although he had been aware of this evidence, Dr Tarn had remained unconvinced, managing to ignore such points as those embarrassing triple splashes and the elevated and exposed fashion in which the oarsmen perched. As far as he was concerned the Lenormant relief showed a 'small open galley that should never have been brought into the business', and that was that.

John did not try to cover the same ground again. He explained how the Lenormant relief should, in his view, be interpreted, and went on to produce an even better card. 'I shall not engage Dr Tarn in detailed argument, since I believe that there is a piece of evidence which he does not take into account, deriving from almost exactly the same period as the [Lenormant] relief and corroborating it in almost every detail.'

As well as checking all known texts John had searched through every recorded fragment of Greek pottery, and discovered one more proof. This other piece of evidence came from an obscure Apulian town, Ruvo, known only for its museum's fine collection of vases, some of which have now been removed to the National Museum of Naples. John recognized the painting on one of these vases as the stern of a trireme, with three levels of oars (fig. 18).

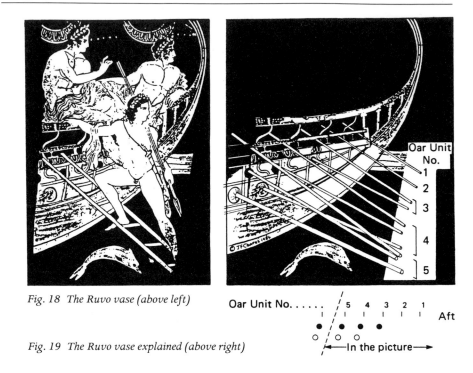

Fig. 18 The Ruvo vase (above left)

Fig. 19 The Ruvo vase explained (above right)

Although one's attention is initially struck by the decorative and lightly clad young men draping themselves around the ship, the vase shows very clearly an outrigger with thole-pins, at which the upper level of oarsmen worked, and two lower levels; it is beyond doubt a three-level ship. Making allowance for perspective, and artist's licence, it looks like fig. 19.

Another interesting point arose when the vase was compared with the Lenormant relief. The bottom row of ports on the vase is larger than the one above it, and they are obviously closed off in some way. The corresponding feature on the relief is a raised blob at the same level. These are the *askomata*, or sleeves, needed to keep water from coming through what were very low ports. The fact that these ports are larger than the ones above, in spite of this being very inconvenient from the point of view of letting in water, is actually a most convincing argument for the accuracy of the vase drawing. We found later – it was not clear when John wrote the article – that this increase in size was needed to allow the oar, which is pivoted nearer the centre of the ship than those at higher levels, to function at all.

John took up two further issues which also changed the whole base of the argument. First, he tackled those Athenian dockyard inventories which described trireme oars as being of only two sizes, very little different in length, and therefore incapable of satisfying those who postulated lengths of anything between 7′ 6″ and 25′.

The real explanation must be, said John, that the shape of the hull required use of these shorter oars in the narrower ends, towards bow and stern, where space was more limited. The odd 8″ would be taken off the inboard end of the oars, the loom, leaving the outboard oar the same length as all the others. As often happened in trireme research, bits of literary evidence corroborated this use of shorter oars at the extremities of the ship: describing the human hand, Aristotle commented that 'the end finger is short rightly and the middle finger long, as in the oar amidships'. The medical writer Galen, who lived in the second century AD when triremes were still common, was even more explicit. 'As I think in *trieres* also the ends of the oars extend the same distance and yet they are not all the same length, for in that case, too, they make the middle oars longest.'

At first sight it seems that this requirement – that all oars in the greater part of the ship should be the same length – makes the matter more complex. It sounds only reasonable that oars higher up in a ship should be longer than those lower down, because they have that much farther to go before they reach the water. So seductively persuasive is this supposition that all previous commentators had made extraordinary efforts to devise oar systems that either avoided three levels or postulated oars of greatly different lengths.

But the evidence was incontrovertible. The official naval list only recorded the two marginally different lengths.

In order to convince the doubters that this was possible John designed a working model (fig. 20) which was built by his father, Sinclair, and illustrated in the same *Mariner's Mirror* article. Linked together, the model oarsmen, scaled to be of contemporary average size in relation to the hull and oars, can be made to operate the oars, all of the same size, quite freely. The wooden rowers move in unison, pulling their correctly dimensioned blades without fouling them or bumping each other or being impossibly restrained by the shape of the hull. The Sinclair Morrison model became the Ark of the covenant of the true believers in the three-tier trireme. Forty years later the same model formed the centrepiece of our first press conference.

Fig. 20 The Sinclair Morrison working model

John Morrison's second point disposed of the old chestnut of numbers – that if a bireme has two levels and a trireme three, the quinquereme must have five, and so forth, up to what might be a quadragintrereme, which is manifestly impossible. A clue to the solution is given by Aeschylus in his play *The Persians*. In it he used an interesting word to describe a trireme – *triskalmos* – which means 'having three thole-pins'. Xerxes himself is made to use it in his final line, as he mourns for 'those who died in the *triskalamoisin*' – the three-thole-pinned ships.

A thole-pin is a vertical bar forming the pivot on which an oar moves: in small boats this function is normally performed by the rowlock. Quite clearly Aeschlyus does not literally mean a boat with three thole-pins, which could only be an odd little dinghy. It must rather mean that the ships which fought at Salamis had three thole-pins where others had only one. John pointed out that the significant factor in the numbering is not the number of levels, but the number of men that can be seated in the space between one oar pivot and the next in line.

Any oarsman needs a minimum clear space if he is to be able to pull his weight. This envelope of space was first described by the Roman architect Vitruvius who called it the *interscalmium*. He defined this longitudinally as the distance between one oar-pivot (rowlock or thole-pin) and the next, being two cubits – the ancient measurement, the length of the forearm from fingertip to elbow. The Attic cubit, as we know from descriptions of temples, equalled 0.444 metres, which is still a reasonable average forearm-to-fingertip for an adult male. In a single-level pentecontor, as in a racing eight, only one oarsman would be accommodated in this two-cubit 'room', as it is known today. The same space in a three-thole-pinner – a trireme – would have to serve for three men on different levels (fig. 21).

Fitting in these extra bodies had important effects on the structure of the ship. The thwarts, which in a pentecontor spanned the entire width of the hull, would interfere with the movements of the two extra ranks;

Fig. 21 The evolution of the trireme

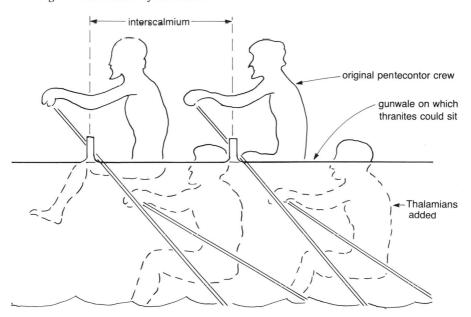

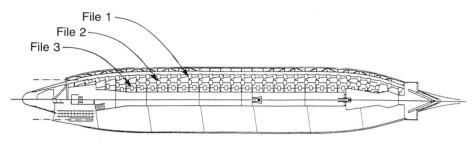

File 1

File 2

File 3

Fig. 22 Classification by longitudinal files

they would have to have been replaced by individual rowing benches, using transverse beams to strengthen an otherwise much-weakened hull.

A hull the same length as that of a pentecontor would therefore be able to carry not fifty but 150 oarsmen, tripling the man-power available to drive the ship. In fact, since the outrigger from which the thranites rowed projected from the hull, even more rowers could be squeezed in. A trireme carried 170 oarsmen – sixty-two thranites (the top level), and fifty-four on each of the other two levels – as was recorded in the Athenian naval lists. Given that the unit space between the thwarts, rowlock or thole-pins remained 0.888 m, the 'engine-room' of a pentecontor, the midships section occupied by the oarsmen, would have been 22 m: allowing one third extra for the great curve of the stern and the forefoot, a pentecontor must have been something like 33 m or 110′ overall. If John's assumptions about the oar system were correct, a trireme must have been of similar size; perhaps rather bigger to allow for increased freeboard, and the ram.

If a hull larger than that were needed, something would have to be increased – beam, length, or depth. The later Greeks did this, and by doing so changed the nature of naval warfare. From being a fast, mobile, ramming machine the trireme evolved into a solider platform for fighting men and machines, and, changing its name as the process developed, deployed increasingly large numbers of men to each oar, whether on two or three levels.

Using Vitruvius's module, John Morrison was now able to advance a rational explanation of ship classification: the numerator referred to the number of men in a 'room'. Two men could each row at different levels in a bireme, three in a trireme. After that oars were multiple-banked; a quinquereme would have two men pulling a blade on each of two levels, with a single-manned oar on the third. Since fifteen men to an oar are known to have been used in Renaissance galleys, it is quite possible, following this system, to explain a 'thirty' or even a 'forty'. Ptolemy's *tesseraconteres* (which sounds better than 'quadragintrereme') with a beam of 47' could have accommodated twenty oarsmen sitting abreast, ten to an oar, or forty on two levels, making it an enormous bireme. Another way of describing the classification is to imagine the ship looked at from above. Longitudinal 'files' of oarsmen would be seen, equal to the number of men in each 'room' (fig. 22).

But the best piece of evidence for John Morrison's theory, and indeed the only unquestioned tangible relic of the trireme, lies in the remains of the sheds that once housed the ships, and which can still be seen today. Shelter from the elements was essential if fragile trireme hulls were to be conserved; they rapidly became waterlogged and slow if left in the water, and required frequent drying out and treatment to preserve their capacity for speed. Sheds were therefore provided at any operating trireme base and remains of a number survive, the most important and well recorded of which are in the ancient port of Piraeus. The twin harbours of Zea and Mounychia, today given over to yachts, are on the southern side of the Piraeus peninsula, facing out over the Saronic Gulf and separated by a steep hill from the modern commercial port.

A block of flats has been built over the relics of the sheds, but they can still be seen in a murky basement, through a grubby mesh screen. A couple of column bases stand in the pavement outside. As remains go, they are not very impressive, but they serve, very importantly, to define the actual size of the vessels, the dimensions of which are confirmed by similar remains in other locations (figs. 23 and 24).

Before the flats were built the size of the sheds was a great deal clearer: they are 47 m (125′ 5″) long and 6 m (19′ 6″) wide (fig. 25). Whatever else is known about the triremes, we can be certain that they had to be of a size to fit inside these sheds, with a little to spare, although it is conceivable that the rams might have projected at one end. Half-way along the Zea waterfront, near the rowing club, some remains of the original harbour stand out. As far as I know these have never been properly described, but they look to me very much like the shoreward end of sheds, and are, at any event, nicer to explore than the correctly authenticated examples.

Fig. 24 Remains of trireme sheds at Zea harbour (above)
Fig. 23 Remains of trireme sheds at Aegina (left)

Given the maximum size of the hull dictated by the dimensions of the sheds it is abundantly clear that 170 oarsmen, each pulling his own oar, could only be packed in by some three-tier arrangement. The idea, as canvassed by Wigham Richardson, that oars were pulled by three men sitting *en echelon* is simply impossible, since it would require a ship much longer than the sheds.

When we got down to designing the trireme we kept coming back to the sheds (fig. 25). They were our one absolutely incontrovertible piece of evidence. We could ruthlessly discard any emendations of the original oar plan which made the ship too big to go into the building, thus disposing of a great number of alternative ideas.

As well as realizing the significance of the vases in the Ruvo museum, John had reviewed everything written by the Greeks themselves about their ship. Putting all these references together is a treacherous job, and one inviting pitfalls, but some reasonably clear conclusions do emerge.

It was clear at least that the trireme was a very fast ship. Thucydides,

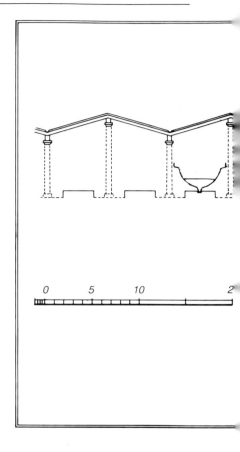

Fig. 25 Reconstruction of complete trireme sheds

a trierarch himself and a stickler for accuracy, described a number of fast contemporary passages: the fact that he did this in such detail certainly implies that they were unusually speedy, not everyday affairs, but also that they were well-attested. The best known of these is the famous dash from Athens to Mytilene on Lesbos made in 427. A Mytilenean rebellion against Athenian rule had been suppressed, and the Athenian Assembly, democratically but viciously, decided to have all the surrendered Mytileneans executed. A trireme was sent to the Athenian commander on Lesbos with orders to that effect, but the very next day the Assembly thought better of its decree, and dispatched another trireme bearing a reprieve. Not stopping at all, the oarsmen eating barley bread mixed with wine and olive oil

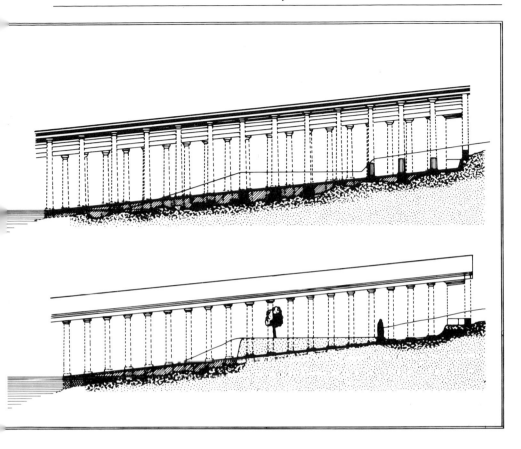

provided by the anxious Mytilenean ambassadors as they rowed, the second ship got there just in time to prevent the massacre. The shortest distance from Athens to Mytilene is $184\frac{1}{2}$ sea miles: the passage was made in twenty-four hours. Another voyage recorded by Thucydides was one of 124 sea miles covered between morning and evening, with a stop for lunch. This was not made by a fresh crew, but by oarsmen who had pulled sixty-four miles on the previous day. More routinely, Xenophon mentions that the voyage from Byzantium to Heraclea on the Black Sea, which is about 129 miles, was 'a long day's voyage' for a trireme under oar. Less specific references to the speediness of these ships are scattered throughout writings of the fifth and fourth centuries, in much the same manner as twentieth-

61

century Englishmen might mention the notorious slowness of the London bus, or the unpunctuality of British Rail.

The use of the trireme in warfare also brings out very positively the characteristics of its design. The earlier, Athenian trireme, with which we were concerned, was built for speed first and last. All other requirements, even sea-keeping qualities, were made subordinate to that. Trireme actions had therefore to be fought in sheltered waters or even in harbours, but never far from land, and always in settled weather. The Battle of Salamis itself took place in a nearly landlocked gulf, a few hundred yards from the shore. The Battle of Artemisium, a couple of weeks earlier, had demonstrated the price that might be exacted from the unwary. Hoping to cut off the Greek fleet, Xerxes had despatched a squadron of 200 ships round the island of Euboea (modern Evvia). A sudden storm blew the ships on to the inhospitable coast of that island, all were wrecked, and more than 40,000 men died in a single night (the Persian ships carried rather larger crews than the Athenian). It was a toll that makes Trafalgar or Jutland seem like petty skirmishes by comparison.

Characteristics of the trireme other than its speed are indicated by dozens of more specific references. One unfortunate trireme commander named Scylax was punished for his failure to post a look-out by being tied up with his head pushed through one of the lower oarports: this gives an indication of the size of the opening. The evidence for absence of bulwarks and a light upper deck – essential for speed – is reinforced when we are told that javelin men were trained to throw from a sitting position. One valuable bit of information which did much to render our own rowers' lives less arduous is Thucydides' mention of oarsmen walking over the Isthmus of Corinth, each with his oar, oar loop and cushion. This reference not only saved a good deal of possible discomfort to our oarsmen, but also settled the one-man-to-an-oar controversy.

The best known and most entertaining proof of the arrangement of the oarsmen in superimposed tiers is that given by the comic playwright Aristophanes in *The Frogs*. The play has many allusions to rowing: Charon, setting the stroke across the Styx, cries 'O opop, O opop'; Dionysius, at the oars, complains of a blistered behind; Aeschylus, in Hades, says that in his time all that trireme oarsmen were able to do was to shout 'yo-heave-ho' and to call for rations; Dionysus agrees, and adds, 'and to fart in the face of the chaps underneath'. (The Penguin translation of *The Frogs*, by David Barret, blushingly omits this passage, and Dr Tarn also thought it too vulgar to consider. But then it did so thoroughly demolish his single-level trireme theory.)

The accumulation of evidence produced by John Morrison in his article in the *Mariner's Mirror* had the effect of a powerful vacuum cleaner in a room cluttered with the dust of centuries (fig. 26); the theories of such trieresophils as Graser, Fincati, Lemaitre, Haack, Busley, Kopecki and Wigham Richardson were politely examined and either disposed of or recast into a single coherent explanation. Unlike these gentlemen, however, Dr Tarn was still very much alive, and refused to be convinced. Commenting in a singularly waspish review he said:

> The author of this article has been reading the old literature about triremes with three superposed banks, and this has produced the common effect of mass repetition; he feels sure that there must, or anyhow might, have been such a thing. So he has taken the Lenormant relief and the Talos vase (I only know this vase from his illustration) and, by assuming that they represent triremes, has from them made a trireme with three superposed banks, a thing neither he nor anyone else would ever have dreamt of extracting from these monuments had he never known of this unhappy theory. . . . Must I really repeat that there is no mention of portholes in Greek, in either texts, inscriptions, papyri, or scholia, nor any word for porthole in the Greek language?
>
> Once I read a really good essay by Mr Morrison, and I am sorry that he should waste his time on this hopeless attempt to recall the thrice-dead to life. Meanwhile, as I seem to be chained to the oar without hope of escape, let me say once more that I care nothing about triremes, but I do care very greatly about the right interpretation and use of evidence.

John was understandably indignant at this ungenerous treatment and still keeps a squib he wrote at the time.

> I do not like thee, Doctor Tarn,
> Though men are old, they still must larn,
> In spite of you my trireme floats,
> And so shall all my other boats.

For the time being the war took precedence, but John returned to the subject, and produced his authoritative book in 1968. *Greek Oared Ships* was the first definitive work on the subject, dealing with the period 900–322 BC, a period which exactly covers the evolution of the trireme, and collating all the textual and archaeological evidence. It became essential reading to all marine historians. Since its publication more archaeological evidence has become available which strengthens the assumptions about three-level oar systems first made by John in 1941. A comparison of his suggested reconstruction published in *Greek Oared Ships* with the one actually built shows how little the outline has had to be changed (figs. 26 and 35).

Tarn was disposed of by John in the introduction to this book, his system being described as 'totally unsupported by any evidence . . . based on the demonstrably untrue assertion that two-level ships did not exist before the *trieres*, and requires furthermore a length of hull and oar which conflicts with the evidence.' *Greek Oared Ships* was a work of such solidity and was so widely accepted that it was astonishing that years later such publications as the *Oxford Companion to Ships and the Sea* had not caught up with it; but this perhaps explains the reason why, when the trireme

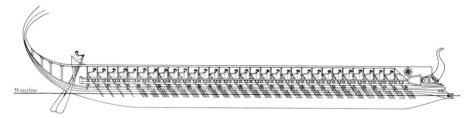

Fig. 26 John Morrison's conjectural drawing, 1963

question was aired in the columns of *The Times*, so varied a range of reactions was elicited.

The letters published in *The Times* in the autumn of 1975 proved the continued existence of diversified views, which were vigorously expressed in a correspondence which still holds the record for size: between 6 September and 4 October 1975, twenty-eight letters, containing some 8,500 words, were published. The correspondence was started by John Morrison in reaction to an article by Eric Leach, which was accompanied by an impression, drawn by Mr Leach, of a trireme under sail in a heavy sea with a following wind. The unfortunate vessel would most certainly have broken her back had not the throng of people on deck previously capsized her: Mr Leach, enthusiastic for the ability of the Greeks as sailors, dismissed evidence that sail was lowered for battle as being:

> all very unconvincing especially when we share the distress of modern rowers exhausted after 17 minutes in the Boat Race – four miles in smooth water, with the tide under them. No, the Greeks were sailors, and professionals at that, and they were sailing for their lives, not for the Auld Mug. They sailed triremes for centuries, improving their techniques and efficiency to serve and protect far-flung colonies.

He denied that oars alone could ever have achieved the speeds that had been recorded in antiquity.

John Morrison was moved to respond, in a slightly miffed fashion: 'I am afraid that if he can believe that he can believe anything . . . The Athenians of Pericles' day were outstandingly fine oarsmen, and fine sailors: they were not so foolish as to take a first class rowing-machine designed for ramming into battle under sail.' He went on:

> Triremes were plainly, as an ancient author says, 'a complicated kind of mill', a rowing-machine designed for high speed and manoeuvrability in the sheltered waters invariably chosen for sea battles, in which the ships were used as rams. When the sea became choppy action was broken off . . .
>
> Thucydides and Xenophon tell us incontrovertibly that mainsails were left ashore before battle. Indeed, on two occasions they were captured by the enemy. Conon captured Lysander's after Aegospotami.

Triremes, he said, could do well enough under oar: '. . . a trireme under oar covered 140 miles in a "long day", i.e., if that is twelve hours, at nearly twelve knots.'

That did it. Mr Leach responded:

> Conflicting it is, indeed. Mr John Morrison has believed what he has read, that a trireme under oar, and without sail, travelled 140 miles

averaging nearly twelve knots. He further believes that much higher speeds would have been possible in short spurts. Perhaps he would like to tell it to the Cambridge Boat Club. If they could break the twelve-knot barrier there would be no more competition from Oxford . . . speeds of around twelve knots would only have been possible under sail. The trireme, as a first class rowing-machine (contradiction in terms) was a non-starter.

John was provoked, and immediately replied:

> Mr Leach . . . seems to claim that when Xenophon says 'under oar' he means 'under oar and sail' – this seems very unlikely. Also, I am much readier to believe Xenophon's precise and unambiguous statement than any guesswork however 'scientific' resting on insecure data and false parallels . . .
>
> But in any case there is absolutely no argument here for Mr Leach's main thesis that the trireme used sail in battle. Is he by any chance the same person as your other distinguished correspondent, Dr Simpliguessverk?

After that the letters began to flow, touching on many topics other than that only of speed under oar, although that was the point of interest to most correspondents. The Vesta Rowing Club was frankly sceptical.

> Though knowing little of the subject in question, and at the risk perhaps of obscuring the real reason for the correspondence, may we query the technical feasibility of propelling, by oar-power alone, a boat over a distance of 140 miles, in twelve hours, at an average speed of nearly thirteen miles an hour? If indeed such a performance was possible, this club will be giving serious consideration to selling our existing racing fleet and converting to triremes.

Mr T. A. G. Raikes disagreed:

> Surely it is a question of acceleration and momentum. In a four-mile race between a trireme and a racing eight, the eight would probably be half-way down the course before the trireme had gained its maximum speed. However, from then on I suspect that the advantage would

be with the trireme whose weight and momentum would keep it going smoothly through the waves, regardless of the movements of the crew. If the race were extended to 140 miles I would put my money on the trireme . . . a very good race could be made of it if a fresh eight took over every four miles or so, relay fashion.

Writing from the St Helier Yacht Club, Mr R. G. Mourant questioned twelve hours as a long day, as well as Xenophon's geography.

Evidently Mr Morrison's Ivory Tower is further inland than his address would indicate, since his basic premises are those of a confirmed lands-man; Mr Leach on the other hand appears to have missed a vital clue.

In the first place, a day at sea is a day of twenty-four hours. A ship does not drift or anchor at night; and a voyage of six days, whether undertaken by Polynesians, Ancient Greeks or Admiral's Cup teams consists of six days and six nights. As seafaring men generally share the fisherman's tendency to exaggerate, 'a long day' might well mean anything from twenty-five to thirty hours. Secondly, the distance from Byzantium to Herakleia (which for all I know may be 140 Statute Miles, if they have ever heard of them in those parts) is certainly less than 120 nautical miles.

Mr Dudley Quirk suggested that the 'long day' might have been dawn to dusk, seventeen hours in high summer, which would bring down the average speed considerably; Mr Humphrey Lynch plumped for fifteen hours. Quinqueremes were quoted; Xenophon was glossed; Mr Hart of Malvern College suggested that just as 'in order to boil eggs by whirling them round your head in a sling as the Babylonians did, it was necessary to be a Babylonian' so, in order to build a twelve-knot trireme it might well be necessary to be an Athenian.

While some correspondents extended the debate into areas such as the likely prevalence of the Etesian winds in the fifth century BC, the design of the quinquereme (of course), the use of hashish as a stimulant (although I thought it was a narcotic), and the nature of Spanish galleys, the weight of the evidence was devoted to a learned analysis of possible maximum speeds. As might be imagined, the expert witnesses differed, and differed monstrously. Mr Desmond Bagley, the well-known writer of adventure stories, proved beyond a peradventure with the assistance of his neighbourhood computer that 1,090 oarsmen would be needed to propel a trireme at nine knots, and 2,050 at ten. Mr M. W. Peters complained that the whole thing could be settled by consulting a yachting diary, and that 2,200 oarsmen would be required to produce a speed of twelve and a half knots.

Professor Gordon of the Department of Engineering and Cybernetics in the University of Reading, drawing on statistics produced during the study of man-powered flight, and 'using the methods of calculation which are customary with naval architects', concluded that 170 oarsmen could propel the ship at eleven and a half knots in short bursts, eight and a half knots as a sustained cruising speed, and 5.7 knots on one bank of oars, while with assistance of sail as much as fifteen knots might be reached. Professor Fitton Brown of the Department of Classics in the University of Leicester was prepared to accept sixteen knots. Mr J. F. Wellicombe of the Department of Aeronautics and Astronautics in the University of Southampton tended to agree: '. . . I see no reason to doubt Mr Morrison's contention that voyages of 140 miles were recorded at speeds approaching twelve knots.'

Mr Humphrey Lynch poured a little more oil on the flames, and insisted that:

> What Xenophon gives us is one of the very few pieces of real evidence bearing on our problem, and it would seem wise to start from that point unless it can be shown to be incompatible with the laws of hydrodynamics and with their application to ancient Greek ship design.

Mrs Nora Wooster appeared as an unreconstructed Tarnite, piously hoping that the by then long-dead scholar was able to follow the correspondence, and relating that her young son had proved that three superimposed banks of oars were 'mechanically unthinkable'.

Lord St David's authorities were very severe, but appear never to have read the classics:

> What is seldom understood about galleys is that they actually spent very little time rowing. They rowed to get out of harbour, or to manœuvre in battle, or in a calm. But Mediterranean and Adriatic calms are usually short and limited to fairly fixed times of day.
>
> The calculations recently produced on galley speeds are interesting, but the naval textbooks reveal that a galley can make four knots for

the first hour, but after that its speed drops by one knot every subsequent hour, so that four hours of rowing reduce it to a standstill.

After that the correspondence was concluded by John Morrison at the invitation of the Editor of *The Times*.

Thank you for giving space to such a fascinating and instructive correspondence. May I try to cast the account? All good men seem to agree to the following:

1. That oared ships did not go into battle under sail.
2. That the Greek trireme used full oar-power to produce up to 11.5 knots in short bursts, only in battle or in emergency.
3. That oared ships did not put to sea when the wind was unfavourable, but rowed out of harbour and then either hoisted sail or continued rowing according to the state of the wind.
4. That a trireme's speed in still water under oar can be credibly calculated to have been five to six knots with one division rowing, a little more with two.
5. And that this calculation does not conflict with Xenophon's '120 nautical miles under oar in a long day'. The word he uses can only mean the hours of daylight. So, with fifteen hours of daylight plus one hour of twilight at latitude 42° on midsummer day the speed works out at seven knots and a half, but there would have been a little help from the current for the last 103 miles. According to the navigation department of the National Maritime Museum, Black Sea currents run counter-clockwise, but through the Bosphorus there is a north–south current because of the 17″ difference of levels at each end. The later MSS of Xenophon have a variant reading 'a very long day', which suggests that the scribe shared your correspondents' feeling that Xenophon was exaggerating a bit. Etesian winds blowing with the current through the Bosphorus would have kept a galley in port.

   Lord St David's galleys were the 'a scaloccio' type of the second half of the sixteenth century, with gangs of men pulling, and in some cases also pushing, very long sweeps. A contemporary admiral reported them slower, in spite of greater manpower, than the earlier 'a zenzile' galleys in which three or four men sat at benches set herringbone fashion each rowing an oar of 30′ or so.

Dr Tarn was rightly impatient of the theory then current that the ships of high numerical denominator in the Hellenistic navies had many banks of oars and suggested instead that the Greeks must have had an 'a zenzile' system for triremes and 'a scaloccio' systems for the rest. The first part of this suggestion has been rejected because:

1. The Greek trireme's oars were $12\frac{1}{2}'$ or $13\frac{1}{2}'$ long (the longest oars amidships and, surprisingly no difference between the levels).
2. An 'a zenzile' galley rowing 100 men would have been far too long to fit into the known length of the Piraeus trireme sheds, the three-level system being (obviously) more economical of space.

There are other more cogent reasons but these two are conclusive. Tarn was quite right about the ships of numerical denominator higher than three. They must have rowed more than one man to an oar at no more than three levels, usually, to judge from the monuments, at two. And the numerical denominator has nothing to do with levels, as people still tend to think: but indicates the power to which the original rowing unit had been raised by the various developments, i.e. 3, 4, 5, 6, men to the oar room, the space between the rowlocks, irrespective of levels. A three-level trireme does not imply a four-level quadrireme.

Two final points:

1. The men who rowed the Athenian galleys in the fifth century were not slaves, indeed slaves who rowed exceptionally well at Arginusae were given their freedom for it.
2. If the hashish-carrying Punic warship reported in your columns is the one about which Miss Honor Frost has recently published some reports, it is too small to be a trireme.
   Yours faithfully,
   John Morrison
   Wolfson College.
   Cambridge.
   October 2

It seemed to me that John Morrison was being a little too sanguine in his conclusions: there did not appear any considerable measure of consensus on, for example, the likely speed of the trireme, since anything between seven and fourteen knots had been quoted. And this estimate, in turn, depended upon the design of the ship itself. If this in any way resembled the monstrosity depicted in the *Oxford Companion* it could hardly have been rowed at all, and certainly at nothing approaching even the lower speed. There had been, moreover, no observations on the vexed three-tier question. My suspicions were later justified, and by the original Mr Leach himself, who wrote to me in August 1986. *The Times*, in reporting the progress of trireme building, had published a photograph of the Greek model, which had clearly been rigged in something of a hurry, giving the impression of proceeding in both directions at once. A letter from me was sent correcting any misapprehensions this may have caused, which provoked in turn a response from Mr Leach:

> Having been involved in the trireme controversy in 1975, I am amazed that anyone could be so enthusiastic about oar propulsion for this type of boat.
>
> No doubt you have explored alternatives to the much publicized and uncritically acclaimed Morrison layout. I enclose my own views (appendices 2 and 3 of a small book I wrote at the time, unpublished).
>
> The Morrison layout would not work very well as I have explained and as can be seen from the amusing photograph published in *The Times*, 4 July 1985. Tests under conditions causing heeling would be conclusively chaotic.
>
> I believe the only time a trireme ever achieved ten knots through the water was under sail. Only then would it look more like a ship than a rolling pin, and only if it were sailed by sailors and not classical scholars.

Mr Leach attached some unpublished papers, the last of which ended in fine rhetorical style: 'The fore-and-aft alignment of all oars, for a trireme, should be left to flourish at the rate of knots only in textbooks: it can do no harm. To produce it on a full scale model would be to perpetrate a one-second folly: the plash of oars, a furrow ploughed, a clattering of blades and a splintering: a stunning silence; disenchantment.'

3

Fully paid-up optimists

By the time I had caught up with the background material my initial after-dinner curiosity as to the nature of the trireme had changed to that much more emotional concern which seems the norm among trireme enthusiasts. It was a ship of engrossing interest; unlike any other reconstruction – the *Argo*, the Kyrenia merchantman then being discussed, or any of the many sixteenth- and seventeenth-century ships already completed, all decent workaday vessels – the trireme was a supreme example of its type. Everything was sacrificed to speed under oar, as in the last English clippers everything had been sacrificed to speed under sail. (The famous *Ariel* was notoriously unseaworthy and eventually disappeared without trace.)

In just the same way the trireme, only able to put to sea in calm weather, fighting only in sheltered waters, and terribly vulnerable to storms, was, like *Cutty Sark*, a *ne plus ultra*, the ultimate of her type. She was a sea-leopard, sleek and powerful, lurking in harbour until ready to dash out and kill. The task of building such a ship after so long an interval would be, however difficult, a rewarding experience.

At this stage any sensible, well-regulated person would have been issuing cautionary messages on the folly of embarking on what would, if it ever came to anything, turn out to be the largest and most complex piece of nautical reconstruction ever attempted. We had no money, patronage or organization, and very little clear information. The founding members of the Trireme Trust were, however, all enthusiasts, and any enterprise entirely so composed is likely to end in either triumph or disaster, although certain to be entertaining on the way there.

John Morrison, and, as I was to discover, John Coates, are as much fully paid-up optimists as I am myself; we were all capable of disregarding the most substantial and well-founded objection to any of our cherished plans. When John Morrison spoke to John Coates, telling him of my suggestion that a reconstruction should be attempted and warning him that the greatest part of the work would inevitably fall upon him, he instantly accepted the suggestion.

Had John Coates then realized how great a burden this would be he might have hesitated. Five years of constant endeavour; two designs; several international conferences in Greece, Denmark, Portugal and the USA; the construction of two full-sized sections and several models of the ship; one Henley Royal Regatta; one International Boat Show; the preparation of a 250-page specification; eighty-six working drawings; negotiations with the Hellenic Navy; arduous supervision of the contractors during building; testing and finally sea trials – all these were to fall to his lot.

If John Morrison is a typical Cambridge don, John Coates could serve as the prototype of the enthusiastic inventor. Tall, spare, immensely active, he is a man of infinite resource, a master of lateral thinking, never long at a loss for an answer to a problem, and never happier than when dealing with a really demanding one. A lifetime spent coping with politicians and shipbuilders has developed in him great reserves of patient wariness: he dreams, I am sure, in conditional clauses.

John Coates's first interest in ancient boats had been stimulated by the remarkable remains found at North Ferriby on the Humber. The oldest ship ever discovered is that of Cheops, found in the Great Pyramid, dating from about 2600 BC, but the North Ferriby ships come a good second. They date from only a thousand years later, and since it is doubtful whether the Cheops boat was ever meant to float or was merely a sepulchral gift, while the Yorkshire boats were certainly well used Humber working boats, we may be able to claim the oldest ships in the world for England.

Although of great technical interest, the Humber ships were rather prosaic large punt-like vessels, used in what must have been an active trade across the river. A reconstruction of one of the North Ferriby boats is projected, and will doubtless be of considerable importance, but it has to be admitted that the prospect of paddling an overgrown punt from Hull to Goole lacks the romantic appeal of dashing in a galley across the wine-dark Aegean. Fortunately for the future of our project, John Coates, at any rate, found it to be so.

The reconstruction could never have been attempted without his participation. John Morrison had succeeded in persuading most of the scholarly world that he had hit upon the right arrangement of oars: the Ruvo vase, the Lenormant relief, and the collation of literary and archaeological references, were sufficient to convince any reasonable person. But this was a far cry from designing a functional ship, a task which demanded the skills of archaeologists, naval architects, craftsmen, and scientists.

As a professional naval architect, John Coates used design principles which apply equally in the design of guided-missile frigates as in ancient oared warships. His professional standing and reputation as designer of the Royal Navy's County Class destroyers was to be as essential in ensuring that our project was taken seriously by the Hellenic Navy as was John Morrison's position as the undoubted authority on the trireme itself.

John Coates had come to triremes some time before through Dr Anderson, the old antagonist of Tarn. In his book *Oared Fighting Ships* Dr Anderson had made some suggestions about oar systems. John's trained eye had spotted something wrong with them: the oar systems suggested in that book nearly all had a gearing – the ratio between that part of the oar outboard of the pivot, and the inboard part where the oarsman pulled – of about 2:1. Such a gearing was only suitable for fairly slow vessels: a fast boat – and triremes were certainly fast – would need a higher gearing, more like that of a racing eight, of 3:1. This may sound a small point, but it was to be a multitude of interacting small points that led us to some major conclusions. If, for example, the trireme oars are the same length, as we knew that they were (always excepting the slightly shorter ones at the ends), a gearing of 2:1 would demand 33 per cent more room inside the boat than a gearing of 3:1, there being that much more of the oar inboard. Conversely a 3:1 gearing would enable the boat using it to be 25 per cent narrower.

Work at the Ministry of Defence kept John Coates from pursuing the matter until after his retirement. Within a month of this he was incapacitated by a severe attack of tennis elbow (brought about, he claims, by undertaking all those jobs about the house that had been left undone for many years). Looking for something that could be done from an armchair he found a copy of John Morrison's *Greek Oared Ships* which included the sketch of a conjectural reconstruction of the trireme. His imagination was fired, like that of many others, by the idea of this sophisticated but mysterious warship, built, like all effective weapons, to the limits of the available technology. He therefore wrote to John Morrison suggesting that they should co-operate on developing the research needed for an actual reconstruction.

Any successful reconstruction certainly demanded as a pre-condition the combination of the very different skills of scholar and ship designer. That was, after all, what Napoleon had tried to do with Jal and de Lôme. Their failure was due partly to a misunderstanding of the evidence, but was rendered inevitable by the lack of consultation forced on them by the Emperor's timetable. This was not an error that John Coates and John Morrison intended to repeat. Their book *The Athenian Trireme* which was published by the Cambridge University Press in 1986 is a careful record of all the considerations behind the reconstruction, and is essential reading for anyone who wants to get to grips with the details of the historical trireme.

If we were going to consider the possibility of building seriously, the not-unimportant question of finance had to be at least approached before much else could be done. This was in the first instance up to me to explore, since I had made the initial suggestion and there was nothing else very useful I could do, being no expert in any relevant subject. I was at the time a director of Grindlay's Bank, which had a substantial connection in Greece with branches in Athens and Piraeus, and was able to ask advice from their experienced manager in Athens. He immediately and wisely poured a measure of accurately cold water upon my hopes of support from the Greek shipping community, who were passing through a bad patch. Following high capital expenditure on super-tankers which were then all rendered redundant by the re-opening of the Suez canal, ship-owners were finding it difficult to make ends meet. There had been some spectacular Greek failures, and most owners would be unenthusiastic about disbursing large sums on so odd an enterprise as ours.

In fact, though we later received generous support from two sources, Eddie Kulukundis and A. P. Vacca in London and George Dracopoulos in Athens, we otherwise failed to interest the ship-owners.

Another colleague on Grindlay's board, Sir Colin Crowe, who had retired from the Foreign Office after a distinguished career, set in motion the interest of his former colleagues by contacting our then Ambassador in Athens. Although just about to leave for Moscow, Sir Iain Sutherland's initial enthusiasm, and the lively support of his successors Perry Rhodes and Jeremy Thomas, and their wives, were to prove of enormous assistance. They appreciated from the outset that what we thought to be an exercise of little more than academic interest would develop into a fruitful and very friendly piece of international co-operation.

At my first meeting with John Morrison we therefore plunged directly into this vital issue of money.

'How much', asked John with the diffidence proper to academics approaching that delicate subject – a diffidence, with John, modified as a result of having assisted in raising enough money to found a Cambridge college – 'do you think it might cost?' I answered with confidence; I had recently finished work on the Royal Commission on the National Health Service examining the financial affairs of what was, regarded as a whole, the biggest corporation in the world, and our report had made much of the importance of accurate budgeting; I was a director of two banks; and fresh from writing a book chastizing with some severity those politicians who were 'slapdash in money matters'. It might therefore reasonably be supposed that I had done a good deal of careful research: such a supposition would however be wholly erroneous.

'Well, I think it costs about £1,000 a foot to build in wood, and we've about 100 feet between perpendiculars. Double it for luck, add a spot for the twiddly bits, and call it quarter of a million.'

This scientific calculation proved to be not much less accurate than most such estimates; the building contract a couple of years later was in the sum of 70 million drachma, about £320,000. But that is not counting the costs of research, development and supervision, which claimed another £100,000. Altogether our original cost projection was only doubled, and our programme merely 50 per cent too short. As a cost overrun that is nothing to what modern defence contractors can manage, as is evidenced by the GEC Nimrod programme, currently a thousand million or so and a few hundred per cent over budget, and several years late.

As well as this piece of careful forecasting we took two policy decisions of some significance. Recognizing that we had no money at all and, in spite of my bold words, no assurance that any would be forthcoming, we must nevertheless not wait to see light at the end of the tunnel before taking our first paces. It might have been prudent to wait until we had gathered funds together before starting work on the project, but instead we decided to move step by step. At each stage we would accomplish something finite which would contribute to our knowledge, even if we had to put up with long intervals between stages. Eventually, we were confident, a replica would be built.

At that time we would, quite properly, have thought it something of an achievement to progress as far as building a full-scale mock-up which, by being rowed in water, would prove the feasibility of John Morrison's oar-system design. As well as the doubts expressed in *The Times* correspondence, some academics still did not believe that our design could work, and something like this would be needed to convince them.

Secondly, we would keep our decision-making unit as small as possible. Three we agreed to be the maximum size for any committee, and since John Coates was much employed with the real work, John Morrison and I living in the same Cambridgeshire village were able to meet frequently and to reach speedy agreement on what should be done.

For the same reason we did not seek out, in the interest of attracting donations, any great and famous names to patronize our Trust, but determined to do what we could by ourselves. The time and effort involved in soliciting the great and famous in the first place, and thereafter in keeping them apprised of our progress, was judged to be better spent in pushing matters forward ourselves.

Edwin Wolff volunteered to act as secretary to the Trust, and Peter Turner, Bursar of Wolfson College, as its treasurer, a task we hoped would prove particularly onerous, at least in the matter of raking in the contributions.

Before going any further I felt it important to sound out for myself the likely extent of any general support we could expect in Greece. More pressing concerns might be engaging Greek attention, but the trireme is a symbol of real emotional significance to Greek pride, difficult to parallel in British terms. Perhaps because of its history of centuries of decline and occupation, Greece, a nation-state only since the 1820s, has a much livelier appreciation of the glories of its past than has this country; Themistocles, Aristotle, Sophocles and even Byron are Christian names as common in Greece as Kevin and Darren in England. The future of the Elgin Marbles, for example, is an object of passionate concern to Greeks, who have seen so many of their national treasures pass abroad – to Berlin, Munich, Paris and New York as well as London. It would have been quite understandable if the Greeks had been a trifle narked by the presumption of a gang of Englishmen in setting about the design and construction of a Greek ship that had made history when our own forebears were wandering the peat-bogs painted in woad.

Nothing could have been further from the truth. Enthusiasms are international and none more so than that of the trieresophils. Quite apart from any traditional Anglo-Hellenic friendships, we found that a mutual admiration for the phenomenal achievements of ancient Greece, and a common taste for messing about with boats, formed strong bonds. In five years of co-operation that were not without their difficulties, our Greek friends have been magnificently understanding and helpful.

My visit to the National Maritime Museum in Piraeus in June 1982 was my first experience of this. Piraeus is not much frequented by tourists, except for those making for the ferries, but in fact well deserves a visit. The corniche is pleasant even in the hottest weather, and there are two excellent museums, the National Museum, which has some magnificent statuary, and the Maritime Museum, a few blocks away in the ancient harbour of Zea. All visitors to Greece are conscious of its classical period; fewer know much of Byzantine times; and fewer still appreciate the history of modern Greece. Throughout its long history of decline and renaissance, of successive occupations and forms of government, the connecting thread of Greek history is the sea. Greeks have always, perforce and by choice, been seafarers, and the Maritime Museum presents with limited resources but great dedication this central aspect of Greek history. The museum is built on part of the ancient harbour itself, the remains of which are visible in the entrance hall, and its collection goes right through the War of Independence to modern times.

The director at that time was Admiral Makris, every inch a fighting sailor, neat and compact, a man of decision; his hearing is impaired by decades of gunfire, so conversations had to be carried out in a confidential bellow. His first ship had been the cruiser *Averoff*, which has now been preserved at Faliron as the nucleus of a floating nautical collection.

Captain Anastasias Tzamtzis had retired from the Merchant Marine to become Secretary General of the National Maritime Museum of Greece and Inspector of Liberian shipping in Piraeus. He is also, although he does not advertise the fact, an authority on ancient maritime history, with a considerable private library, and is a man of great humour and personal kindness.

The name of John Morrison was an immediate key: there was no question in Captain Tzamtzis' mind that John was the authority on triremes. He was well acquainted with *Greek Oared Ships*; there were three copies in Greece, and the Captain knew the whereabouts of them all.

He also told me of the formation of the Hellenic Institute for the Preservation of Nautical Tradition (HIPNT), run by a yacht-broker, Harry Tzalas, which was then organizing the construction of a replica of a fifth-century cargo ship, based upon a wreck discovered off Kyrenia. The reconstructed Kyrenia ship was intended to join the *Averoff* in the new Maritime Museum at Faliron.

Four years later, as the trireme was nearing completion, I asked Anastasias Tzamtzis what his reaction had been when our idea was first put to him. The politest of men, he was a little diffident about admitting that it had been one of complete scepticism. At the time of my first visit, however, this was well disguised and the Director and Secretary General assured me of their support for our idea, a promise that they fulfilled many times over in the next few years.

Fortified by their willingness to accept a British initiative and by their enthusiasm for the idea, whatever their private reservations, we were able to contemplate making our venture public.

The capacity of the trireme to attract the liveliest of interest had already been proved by *The Times* correspondence, and I was sure that, properly briefed, at least the middle-class English newspapers would give a good coverage to our reconstruction project. But I was also aware of the need for a professional and organized approach to be made, and accordingly sought the help of John Addey.

John Addey is well-known in the field of financial public relations; he knows most people in the newspaper world and has built up a reputation for straight dealing and producing interesting stories. We had worked together some years before on a contested takeover bid, which had led to dissenting rumblings that continued over a long period. Nothing could be further removed from the complexities of takeover and merger politics than the trireme, but John Addey is a cultivated man and a phil-hellene, who had lived in Byron's chambers in Albany, and had a considerable Greek acquaintance. Fully realizing that this would bring a great deal of work unaccompanied by financial benefits, he threw himself into the arrangements with his usual panache.

Our first press conference was held in his office in Wardrobe Court in August 1982. All the Johns – Morrison, Coates and Addey – were there, and the project was ceremonially unveiled. At that time all we could produce was John Morrison's forty-year-old model and a few preliminary drawings from John Coates, but, given the expansive – and completely unwarranted – confidence with which we all spoke of the project, it was enough. Not only the posh papers, but radio, television and the wire services were excited. As I was the jack of all trades, a good deal of the trotting about

79

immediately following the press conference fell to me. For the first time I penetrated that part of Broadcasting House given over to Radio 2, and realized that one's whereabouts in that building could be ascertained by observing the dress of the staff; jeans and sweatshirts in Radio 2, tweeds and sports jackets in Radio 3, and suits – even dog-collars – in Radio 4. What goes on in Radio 1 remains a mystery. It was made clear to me, too, that although the piece from Aristophanes might be quoted in the unexpurgated version on Radio 3, the young listeners on Radio 2 would have to have it rendered as 'break wind'.

Newspaper clippings came in from all countries and the most unlikely of publications. We might have expected *Katherimina*, the Athenian equivalent of *The Times*, to give us a sympathetic coverage, but *Nice Matin*? The *Christian Science Monitor*, yes – but the *Lahore Daily Bund*?

Our collective breath was taken away, and even John Addey was impressed, by the number of press cuttings. Even if our initial approach had been somewhat lighthearted, we accepted that we were now all personally committed to pushing the project forward.

The first step was to put the so-far tentative conclusions of John Morrison and John Coates to the trireme community in order to elicit informed comment. So that the critics could have something to chew over, and the practicability of the three-tier system could be finally established, we decided to build a full-scale mock-up of a section of the ship, with six rowing positions, two on each level, which would be capable of being operated in a tank of water. Nothing short of this would convince the doubters that the oar system would work, but if it did we could be sure that we were on the right track.

The oar system was central to the whole project, as it had been central to all disputes about the trireme between the one-levellers and three-levellers, the single and triple benchers, for the past 400 years. Although the Sinclair Morrison working model indicated that such a system was possible, proving this with real live people in wet water was quite another thing.

One factor that had to be considered was the relative size of fifth-century Athenians and contemporary Englishmen, a subject almost as productive of controversy as the trireme itself. Would we perhaps have to find 170 persons of restricted growth to crew our ship, if it turned out too small for more standard-sized oarsmen?

There is a popular feeling that humans have grown perceptibly larger over the ages, and there is a good deal of support for this in recent British history. In the early nineteenth century Walter Scott was able to refer to a character as a veritable giant 'fully 6 feet tall'. Thackeray, in *Pendennis*, stresses the heroine's unusually tall stature; she is 5′ 6″. At the beginning of the First World War the average English soldier was a mere 5′ 6½″ (the Germans, after a generation of health insurance were a good deal bigger and stronger). Since then the average height and weight has increased very considerably. It is also true that modern Greeks are noticeably, on the average, shorter than Englishmen.

A further argument in favour of trireme crews being short was the element of selection involved. The cream of Greek society would have chosen to fight as cavalry, or as hoplites – heavy infantry, providing their own expensive weapons. Being the cream, they would also have tended to be larger. Even in societies that do not rely on personal prowess in hand-to-hand fighting, the upper classes tend to be bigger than others: in England today the average height of the senior grades in the civil service is reported as being significantly greater than that of the lowest. Serving in a trireme was altogether a less elevated role than that of the hoplite, although the thranites regarded themselves, and were regarded, as being a cut above the others.

On the other hand, there is a touching record of the fact that before the Battle of Salamis the young cavalrymen of Athens, realizing that their traditional arm would be useless against the Persian masses, went to the temple of Athene where they hung up their bridles as a dedication to the goddess, and then walked away to take up the less socially elevated, but more essential, task of pulling an oar.

I did not find myself swayed by the arguments in favour of miniscule Greek oarsmen: it might well be that in any given society average growth has increased over the years, but that tells one nothing about any other society: while if average growth has been increasing at all steadily our forebears must have been very small indeed. The length of the Athenian cubit (see p. 55) does not suggest that this was so. Furthermore, the Mycenaean weapons in the Athens National Museum, which date from nearly a millenium prior to our period, are large, the sword-blades, for example, being a good yard long. Such weapons could only have been effectively handled by big men; but then the class/size argument could be brought to bear there, as well as the racial differences between Mycenaeans and the later Dorian invaders.

It did seem, on enquiry, that there was little evidence to support the received opinion that human dimensions have steadily increased over the centuries. Stature has fluctuated according to racial mixtures, diet, urbanization and other factors. It is quite true that children tend to be taller than the average of their parents' heights, but this secular trend is very small. It is also true that the present generation of Europeans is the tallest ever, but even so it has done little more than recover the ground lost since Roman times.

One of the few studies that I found came from Denmark and threw up the following figures:

Period	Average male height (cms)
Mesolitithic	161.50
Early Neolithic	165.60
Late Neolithic	176.20
Bronze	172.00
Roman	177.40
Viking	171.20
Middle Ages	172.60
Seventeenth/eighteenth centuries	174.00
1850	165.00
1908	169.00
1982	179.00

So it seems that although modern man is substantially taller than his immediate forebears he is only an inch or so more than his late Stone Age ancestor. Unfortunately not much work has been published on Greek anthropometry, but there is no reason to suppose Bronze Age Greeks were much different to Bronze Age Danes; the relative prosperity and consequent better diet of Denmark would explain why contemporary Greeks are still, like the Danes earlier this century, shorter in stature.

As well as the question of relative height – to say nothing of musculature, which introduced an added complexity – which might make it hard to validate John Morrison's theories in a full-scale model, there remained a body of opinion unconvinced by John's arguments.

Prominent in this was Dr Lucien Basch, a Belgian lawyer and a frequent contributor to the trireme debate, with a particular interest in Phoenician triremes which he insisted were quite different from those of the Greeks. Dr Basch had published his views in some decidedly acerbic articles: 'Morrison has made the mistake of relying on secondary sources.' 'Morrison is not easy to understand.' 'What are the true reasons advanced by Morrison in support of . . . I have sought in vain but there are none.'

Less crossly, a Dutch scholar, Andre Sleeswyk, had put forward alternative explanations both of which embodied a complex turret-like arrangement. Sleeswyk was worried about the problem of metacentric height, and since this presents a real difficulty a brief explanation of the principles involved becomes essential. The hull of any ship has a centre of gravity which is determined by the weight of the hull. When the hull is upright the centre of gravity will lie on the centre line of the ship; and the lower down it is the more stable the ship will be. When the ship rolls to one side, which as poor sailors know is a regrettably frequent occurrence in inclement weather, the centre of gravity shifts also. Metacentric height is the measure of the ability of the hull to right itself after rolling, and the higher it is, the 'stiffer' or more stable the ship will be (fig. 27).

The light hull of the trireme, and the necessity of carrying three tiers of oarsmen above the waterline, meant that its centre of gravity was bound to be high, the metacentric height uncomfortably low, and the ship therefore relatively unstable. To be sure, stability could be improved by carrying ballast, but this would be at the cost of reducing the speed, thus negating the point of the extra tiers of oarsmen. In an interesting article in the *Scientific American* of April 1978, Foley and Soedel estimated the metacentric height of a trireme at 0.4 m, which they believed only 'marginally adequate'. Sleeswyk calculated that by seating the two upper rows of oarsmen lower than we were planning, the metacentric height would increase by about 0.10 m to 0.15 m, 'resulting in a substantially more stable ship'. If his ideas met the test of the evidence we would have to think again.

Proving the oar arrangement, and exposing the results to the criticism of anyone who showed an interest, was therefore important to us, but only the first step in our reconstruction. It would show one way in which ship might have been propelled but would leave the vital question of the shape of the hull still to be settled. At this stage John Coates had only sketched out some preliminary thoughts, and had not been able to go into any detail about how the ship was put together.

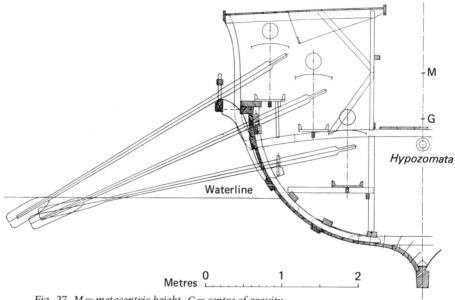

M = metacentric height
G = centre of gravity
Hypozomata
Waterline
Metres 0 1 2

Fig. 27 M = metacentric height, G = centre of gravity

We were still feeling our way through four centuries of dissension and speculation, with the sparsest of facts on which to rely. At the conference we planned anyone at all interested in the trireme question would be welcome to criticize our ideas and give us their own views on any aspect of the reconstruction. Having seen something of triremers by then, I felt that they would seize on the opportunity with alacrity.

PART II

4

Adventure playground

Our projected conference was arranged for April 1983. The Director of the National Maritime Museum at Greenwich, Dr Basil Greenhill, very handsomely allowed us to hold it at that appropriate location.

Since the purpose of the mock-up was limited to proving that the oar system would work when reproduced in full scale, there was no point in our attempting to duplicate classical methods of construction. As long as the dimensions were correct we could put the section together out of anything that came in handy, but as it was quite large (equivalent to about one-twentieth of the total ship) building it would nevertheless come expensive.

John Coates finished the drawings of the mock-up in November 1982, leaving little enough time for it to be made and tested before the April conference; and there was the matter of money. A quotation of £10,000 was obtained from a reluctant firm, not at all anxious to embark on so unusual a job; we would have been hard put to scrape up £100.

This was the point when we found that John Coates was not only a distinguished naval designer but an accomplished improviser who had many willing friends and neighbours. He decided to build the mock-up himself with the help of another retired naval constructor, David Moss, who had previously been general manager of Portsmouth Dockyard. They found some second-hand timber and started work in the Coates's garden in Bath. Although this was by then the depth of winter everything had to be done in the open, since the mock-up was too large to fit in any available workshop. Being in effect a full-sized slice through one half of the ship, it measured about 2 m by 2.5 m.

Coates and Moss managed to get the work finished on schedule, but without time for there to be thorough preliminary testing of the completed section. John managed to borrow some oars from a nearby school, but these were shorter than they should have been, and proper proving was impossible until we got the contraption to Greenwich. The problem of transport from Bath was solved by stripping down the mock-up to its constituent parts, packing it into John Morrison's aged horse-box, and towing it, rather slowly, to London behind an even older Land-Rover.

At that time we were still worried about whether enough space was available inside in which to operate the oars, and although we wanted skilled oarsmen we thought that the average British rower might be too large. Accordingly six members of the Cambridge University lightweight crew agreed, with some reservations, to row in front of our assemblage of notables at Greenwich.

I, for one, awaited their arrival with some trepidation. It was going to be a very public spectacle in front of press, radio and television as well as our collection of trireme savants. Mock-up, water, crew and oars would come together for the first time on the morning of the conference itself. The ghost of Sir William Woodthorpe Tarn would doubtless be highly amused if young Mr Morrison's system turned out to be a complete flop.

The company that assembled at the National Maritime Museum was impressive. We had succeeded in attracting an international force – France, Holland, Greece, Denmark, America – and gathering some of the best-known names in the arcane field of nautical archaeology. As well as a contingent from the National Maritime Museum itself, Anastasias Tzamtzis and Harry Tzalas, Themistocles Tipaldos and John Sakellarides from the Hellenic Society for Research and Invention, and George Dracopoulos a ship-owner who has founded a maritime museum in Mytilene, had all come from Greece. Vice-Admiral Sir Simon Cassels could speak for the Royal Navy, James McMillan for the working boat-builder, and Mike Pullen, an experienced oarsman, for the Amateur Rowing Association. Tim Severin, then working on his *Argo* project, was able to take time off to see what we were up to. Most importantly Richard Steffy of the University of Texas had agreed to analyse our suggested design.

Dick Steffy's position as an acknowledged expert on ancient ships of the Mediterranean, and his recent experience, were so particularly germane to our project that it was not going too far to say that if Steffy disapproved of any aspect of our ship we would have to go back to the drawing-board.

He saw the whole thing in an historical perspective, which he calls 'structural philosophy' – the reasoning behind the methods of construction.

> In different periods of history, shipbuilders fulfilled physical laws by using different technological approaches. The method of approach – the philosophy – was influenced by a myriad of factors such as available materials, economics, trade patterns, geography, politics, religion, and even historial perspectives. For instance, modern freighters utilize these factors differently from ships of a century ago.
>
> Whether structural philosophies change with the introduction of new materials or vice versa is not important; we are only interested in the fact that each ship-type in each historical period is accompanied by a compatible philosophy.

Professor Steffy's work, following this thesis, enabled us to integrate information gathered from different types of ship, giving us reasonable indications of the methods by which our trireme would have been constructed.

On the day of the conference itself, conscious of the distinguished and learned guests arriving at the Maritime Museum, I was not filled with confidence by the first sight of the mock-up. It was only a slice out of the hull, so quantities of internal beams and joists, which would not exist in the ship itself, were needed to hold it together. These further restricted an already cramped space and made getting on to a rowing-bench an acrobatic exercise. Nor was the expression on the faces of the Cambridge crew encouraging when they arrived and saw something resembling part of a fiendish adventure playground tethered alongside what looked like – and indeed was – a child's paddling pool. The impressive backdrop provided by the Museum buildings made the whole thing even more Emmett-like by contrast. Fortunately things had been so managed that the scholars were busy in the lecture hall and the newspapers and television were not yet due. At least they had time to practise a little, taking things very gently.

I should have had more faith. The oarsmen were insinuated into their climbing-frame, and after a few preliminary curses and splashes began to move the blades in unison (fig. 28). It worked. Our euphoria was considerable, and soon transferred itself to the journalists and television crews. The first part of the great trireme puzzle had been solved. The ghosts of Wigham Richardson, Tarn, and all the others were laid. A three-tier oared ship could work.

Fig. 28 The mock-up rowed at Greenwich

But this was by no means the same as proving that our oar system was the one that had been used in ancient times; other methods might also be possible. And even if we had hit upon the right method of propulsion, we were still a very long way from being able to set about building a ship.

John Morrison's original reconstruction of the oar system had been based solely on the tenuous evidence of the Lenormant relief and the Ruvo vase, with what support could be found from written sources. When it came to designing the hull we had even less to go on: the only truly reliable information was the size-limit imposed by the dimensions of the trireme sheds. Some

90

more guidance was, however, now made possible by new techniques of underwater archaeology. Skin-divers working in the moderately warm and clear waters of the Mediterranean have turned up some remarkable finds in recent years. The most helpful, from our point of view, was the discovery by Honor Frost in 1974 of timbers that seemed to belong to a warship of the third century BC. At first it was thought that this might be a trireme, which occasioned considerable excitement, but it soon became clear that the ship was of an altogether later type, the liburnian, a fast thirty-four-oared galley with two men pulling each oar. Although this particular specimen was Carthaginian, the same type of ship was used at the same time – around 300 BC – by their Roman opponents. She carried ballast and was therefore meant to be used frequently under sail, but she was undeniably an oared warship, and the nearest thing to a trireme that we were likely to come across.

The decaying timbers of the Marsala ship – it is generally so known after the Sicilian town where it is now inadequately stored – do not appear particularly striking to the uninitiated but reveal a great deal to the experienced boat-builder. Among much interesting information that has been discovered – including the fact that the ship's stores included hashish – the most significant find was the stern section of the keel. The keel is the backbone of a ship, from its depth, its shape, and the fashion in which other timbers are joined to it, the rest of the hull can be reconstructed. Since the Marsala ship's keel was recovered nearly intact, we hoped to learn much from it that would be relevant to trireme design.

One school of thought had advanced the theory that the trireme should have a keel gently curved throughout its length in the fashion of a rocking-chair, and therefore known as a 'rocker keel'. While such a keel is suitable for a sailing-ship, helping to provide longitudinal strength in the hull, it was the last thing we wanted to see in a trireme, as it would make it very difficult to fit in our oar arrangements, which depended on keeping all three levels in a straight line. Havoc would be created if oarsmen had to be fitted into a hull which was anything but parallel between keel and deck. We were therefore very pleased to find that the Marsala ship had a straight keel with a sharp rise aft, which made it altogether more suitable both for rowing and the constant beaching which we know triremes underwent.

Another wreck discovered at the same time was a century nearer our date. This was a fourth-century hull, remarkably well preserved, found off Kyrenia in Cyprus (fig. 29). The Kyrenia ship was admittedly a round-bilged

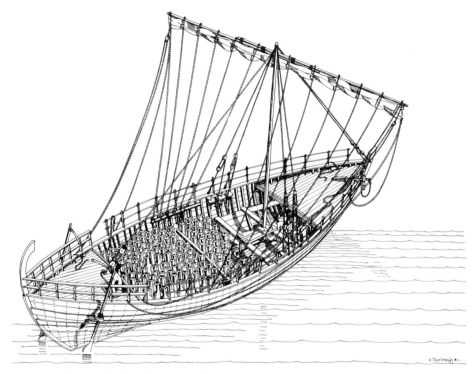

Fig. 29 Sketch of the Kyrenia merchantman

merchantman, a sailing-ship designed for duties entirely different from those of such light and speedy warships as the trireme. But just as modern frigates and container ships are built using the same techniques of plate-forming and welding, so all ancient ships – and enough fragments of later vessels have been discovered to substantiate this – were constructed by the shell-first method exemplified in the Kyrenia vessel.

The principles of classical ship-construction are therefore well enough known. Modern boats are built by first making stout frames which are subsequently clad with planks either overlapping (clinker) or simply placed edge to edge (carvel). Ancient vessels, however, followed a quite different method, being constructed from the outside in – the shell-first method (fig. 30). After laying the keel the sides were formed by carefully joining the planks together, edge to edge, using many mortice-and-tenon joints pegged in. Thereafter this skin was reinforced by light frames inserted as the

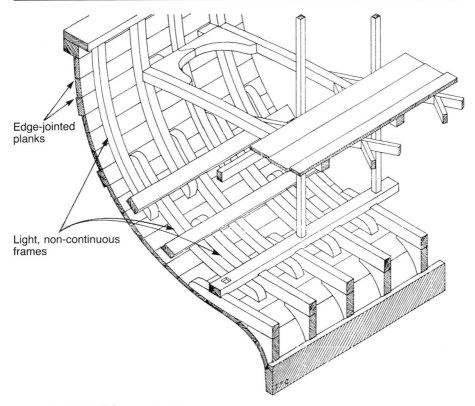

Edge-jointed
planks

Light, non-continuous
frames

Fig. 30 Shell-first construction

work continued. In coach-building terms this is not dissimilar to the difference between a heavy chassis carrying a body fabricated from panels,
and a monocoque body where the whole is an integral unit. Such light classical hulls were well adapted to being rowed in the generally calm waters
of the Mediterranean, but would have had a hard time of it in the North
Sea or the Atlantic. Nor, of course, would they have stood up to the stresses
imposed by the use of artillery.

The question of fastenings was central to the design of ancient ships.
The larger members of the hull – the keel, stem and stern and main frames
– were spiked in much the same way as they are today, but using bronze
spikes driven through wooden dowels rather than galvanized iron. But the
method of joining the planks edge to edge is altogether different from any-

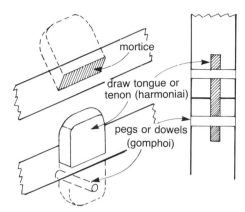

Fig. 31 Mortice-and-tenon jointing

thing practised today. It consisted of cutting a mortice slot in the two adjoining planks, inserting a tenon (the draw-tongues or *harmoniai* in Greek) into the slots, and securing it by driving a dowel (pin or *gomphos*) through it (fig. 31). In order to secure the integrity of the hull and the planks, the joints had to be a very tight fit, and there were rather more than 20,000 of them to be made in the trireme.

Being a merchantman, the Kyrenia ship was not, any more than a modern freighter, built to the same narrow tolerances that might be expected of a high-performance warship; although the principle of construction was the same, the freighter's builders did not need to concern themselves with achieving maximum lightness and speed. The wreck was, considering its age, in a fine state of preservation: some three-quarters of the hull, including the whole of the keel, stem, frames and planking to above the waterline, and even the lead sheathing, had been preserved by being buried under the cargo of amphorae.

As with the *Mary Rose*, some 2,000 years younger, the Kyrenia ship and its contents opened a window on the seafaring of the time. Tools, fishing tackle, equipment and crockery, even the remains of the crew's last meal (olives, figs, grapes and garlic, doubtless accompanied by bread or porridge), were recovered.

Recovering and reassembling the Kyrenia ship was a work of immense skill and complexity, carried out under the direction of Dick Steffy and the Institute of Nautical Archaeology in Texas and taking the better part of eight years. By 1974 the hull was reassembled under cover in Kyrenia but the events of that year – the Greek Cypriot attempted coup under the egregious Mr Sampson followed by the Turkish invasion and the *de facto* division of the island – isolated the remains of the ship from Greek scholars.

One fortunate effect of these unhappy circumstances was that the Greeks decided to build a modern replica and announced this project in November 1982, shortly after we had decided on our own attempt. Harry Tzalas, the ebullient president of the Hellenic Institute for the Preservation of Nautical Tradition (the HIPNT), was the moving spirit behind this, with the help of Professor Michael Katzev, vice-president of the Institute of Nautical Archaeology and a well-known underwater archaeologist, who had carried out the first work on the Kyrenia ship.

With the copious information available, their reconstruction, *Kyrenia II*, was able to go ahead quickly, so providing us with a test bed to observe any difficulties that might be encountered. Even more valuable, Harry Tzalas's reserves of enthusiasm were sufficiently great to allow him to take an active and friendly part in our own project.

The other discovery, although much smaller, was of equal importance. Remains of oared warships have proved elusive, since in order to keep the weight down they carried little or nothing in the way of ballast or stores. What ancient wrecks have been found have been preserved by being buried in the sea bottom under their own cargo; a light warship would merely, under such conditions, fragment and disentegrate. Apart from the Marsala wreck only one relic of an undoubted oared warship has so far turned up. The entire bronze ram which was found off Atlit near Tel Aviv in 1980, although not quite of the right period – being from the middle or end of the fourth century BC – nor of the right country – being Phoenician rather than Greek – nor even of a trireme – but a heavier warship, one of the later quinqueremes or bigger – nevertheless gave information that was of vital help. Again it was Dick Steffy who analysed the ram, which contained some surviving timbers. These were edge-jointed in the same way as the merchantmen had been, and proved that this method of construction, of which a good deal was known, could be adopted for the trireme. The size and strength of the timbers indicated the form of the remainder of the hull which formed, in Professor Steffy's words, 'a giant arrow', with longitudinal strengthening wales running the whole length of the ship, reinforcing the ram and forming the shaft of the arrow (fig. 32). The configuration of the remaining timbers gave some clues as to the likely shape of the hull.

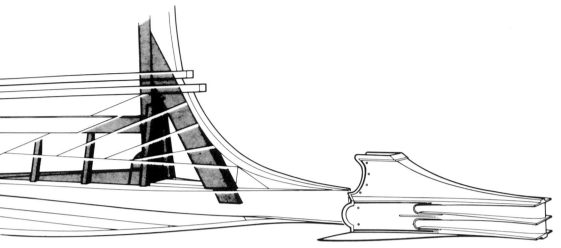

Fig. 32 'A giant arrow' – drawing of the Atlit ram

Given that we knew how the frame of our ship was fitted together and would know more of the potential pitfalls as the Kyrenia reconstruction advanced, and assuming that we had hit upon the right oar system, our major problem remained that of designing a trireme that would perform as well as we knew that the classical ship had done. We might have got the engine-room right, as it were, but this was only a beginning. No one knew anything for certain about the hull of a trireme: some representations of both ends existed, but little of what went in between. Previous commentators in the great trireme debate had, with a single exception, concentrated on the oar system and paid little attention to the form of the hull. The exception was hardly encouraging, since even with all the resources of the French Empire and the services of the greatest naval architect of the time, Louis Napoleon had entirely failed to build a ship that actually worked.

It might not be too difficult to design a galley that would float and be capable of being managed at sea; Colin Mudie had done so effectively enough with *Argo*. But as well as being much larger than a 14–20 oared galley, the trireme was above everything a fast ship; time after time in Greek literature the point had been hammered home that Athens was the home of the fast triremes and that speed was as important as in a race-horse. The historians had recorded details of specific performances: a successful reconstruction had to be capable, in the right hands, of matching these, and doing so within the limits of the technology that had been available at the time. Any reconstruction, however closely it accorded with the available evidence, that was capable only of being rowed slowly, and for a short time, would have to be accounted a failure.

We had to set about designing our ship with only a miniscule amount of real evidence, relying on the principles of physics and hydrostatics, and testing each step to ensure that it accorded with whatever was known or could be reasonably conjectured.

Another piece of physics is necessary to the understanding of the main design problems we faced. Modern fast boats, whether power or sail, rely for their maximum speeds on liberating themselves from the water by heaving themselves up as much as possible and skimming along the surface, an action known as 'planing'. The most advanced form of this is seen in hydrofoils where at speed the whole of the hull is raised, with only the foils remaining in the water. Larger vessels cannot do this, and are subject to the laws governing the motion of a solid body through a fluid; such hulls are referred to as 'displacement' hulls.

The achievement of high speeds from a displacement hull depends on a number of factors. The most obvious of these is that the resistance encountered from the water must be minimized. This can be done first by ensuring a streamlined entry of the hull into the water, and designing the exit so that the least disturbance is created; and, second, by having as little as possible of the ship below water. Streamlining is reasonably straightforward: the general outline of a galley hull is depicted so often that there can be little scope for going wrong providing these examples are followed. Keeping the below-water area to a minimum necessitates the interplay of complex design factors.

The lighter the hull, the higher it floats, with more out of the water; a triangular below-water surface will be smaller than a rectangular; a shorter hull exposes less than a longer. But the fulfilment of each of these criteria brings other results. A super-light hull will not have sufficient strength to cope with the varied stresses that may be expected; too little below the waterline will make the ship unsteady; a fast displacement hull must be of a certain minimum length. This is because, as a ship moves through the water, it creates waves which can be seen lapping along the sides. At low speeds these waves are short both in length and height, but as speeds increase they grow larger in both dimensions, causing a big bow wave that gives rise to the expression 'going with a bone in her teeth' to describe a fast-moving vessel (the Zeebrugge ferry disaster probably occurred when increasing speed raised this bow wave to a height where it entered the open bow doors).

When this first wave becomes so long that the stern of the ship finds itself in the trough of its own power wave, her trim changes; she goes up at the bow and down at the stern, literally creating a slope of water up which she has to climb. As the propulsive energy becomes diverted from pushing the ship forward into countering this wave effect, the ship's speed drops off. The longer the hull, the longer it takes for the bow wave to develop, and therefore the faster the ship can go before reaching its maximum speed.

The formulation of this phenomenon – that the speed of a ship increases in proportion to the square of the waterline length – was not established until the nineteenth century, but it had long been known to ship-builders that longer ships could go faster than short ones, other things being equal. The pentecontor, with its twenty-five oarsmen a side, was just about as long as could then conveniently be built in wood. Inside a hull of similar dimensions the trireme packed more than three times that manpower.

This did not constitute a pure gain producing a proportionate increase in speed; there was the corresponding penalty of the increased weight of another twenty tons or so of humanity and equipment. In order to counteract this increase the fabric of the ship itself had to be reduced to the absolute minimum and any excess weight sheared off in the interests of speed. Though the edge-jointed construction made for a strong light hull, this was going too far; especially since the strength of the original hull had been reduced by removing the thwarts. No wooden hull of the size and fragility of the trireme could hold together without some further support. The trireme was therefore equipped with structural reinforcement by means of the hypozoma. This mysterious object deserves a section to itself (see page 112). It was a rope of some sort that held thc ship together in some fashion, and it caused a great deal of puzzlement.

Since John Coates set about designing a trireme to match known performance criteria, the theoretical qualities of the design could be tested as we went along, so that at each stage we would be able to confirm their validity. But at the same time the design had to accord with all the available evidence. It must fit into the ship sheds, must have an oar system that met the criteria, and must satisfy all the scattered facts that John Morrison had collected. If it proved impossible at any time to develop a design that would perform adequately within these restrictions we would know that we were barking up the wrong tree and would have to begin again.

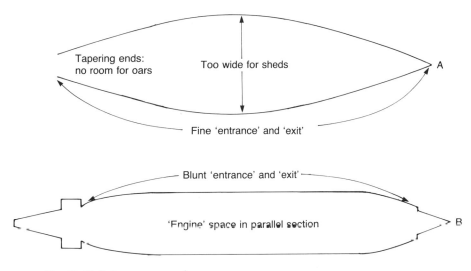

Fig. 33 Hull shapes compared

At the very beginning of his work John came up against a difficulty. A fast hull is likely to taper progressively from midships to either end, but it was immediately obvious that such a hull would either have to be too broad in the middle to fit into the ship sheds, or too narrow at the ends to allow the lower two files of oarsmen to work side by side (fig. 33A). So we would have to 'fill out' both bow and stern to make room for the rowers, while keeping the midships section narrow enough to fit, however closely, into the trireme sheds (fig. 33B). These formed the one piece of hard evidence which must not be neglected, and to which all our designs must conform.

But could such a hull, with bluffer entrance and exit lines, then be made fast enough? We had unimpeachable evidence that a trireme could, under pressure, keep up an average speed of seven and a half knots for twenty-four hours. A theoretical estimate of the energy that would be needed to overcome the resistance and achieve such a speed was not too difficult to make, but the input available had to be defined. The source of this energy was human beings exerting their muscle power. What horsepower could be expected from our oarsmen? The trireme correspondents to *The Times* had made some sweeping assumptions about the work output of an oarsmen, but accurate information was essential and difficult to come by. John Coates had to start from scratch by delving into physiological papers on the performance of oarsmen and other athletes, penetrating such mysteries as aerobic rate, kilo calories, and the mathematics of intermittent work. Apart from nineteenth-century studies of the output of Irish labourers turning winch handles, the most helpful was a modern book, the *Textbook of Work Physiology*. From these varied sources John calculated that, even with the bluffer-ended hull, a crew of 170 could produce enough energy output to maintain the necessary speed, 'eating at their oars and sleeping in turns'. Practical proof of this would only come when our trireme was rowed by an experienced crew, but balancing these requirements to produce such a ship would require very precise calculation when it came to the detailed design work.

Before we were able to gather together all the opinions and information at Greenwich, the only facts we could be reasonably sure of were:

1. There were 170 oars, measuring 9 and 9.5 cubits long.
2. Each man had his own oar.
3. The ship could not be bigger than 5.50 m beam and 36 m length, in order to fit the sheds.
4. The construction was that universally used at the time and for centuries after; a shell-built hull, the planks joined edge to edge with tongues pegged into slots.
5. Two oddities: the seats must accommodate the greased cushion known to have been carried by each oarsman, and the lowest port had to be large enough to shove Scylax's head through.
6. The hull was to be strengthened by the hypozoma, which formed an essential part of the ship's equipment: what it was, where it went, and what it was made of, we still had no idea.
7. The ship must be able to sail reasonably well in favourable winds, and attain continuous high speeds under oar.

Little enough, but also restrictive enough to rule out many possibilities, which was helpful. The fewer the choices the easier it would be to choose. The single fact that the length of the oars was as described in the navy lists was enough to put paid to any of the more picturesque solutions which demanded much shorter thalamian oars. Since the oar system used in the mock-up had in fact worked we could regard ourselves as having eliminated any very different possibilities.

However, even these facts, which we assumed to be incontrovertible, could be questioned: people still find it very difficult to believe in equal-length oars, and constantly try to find a way round that. Some critics, headed by Dr Lucien Basch, remained sceptical. The evidence of the sheds was criticized as only establishing the *maximum* dimensions: a trireme could, it has been said, be narrower. (The fact that this would result in a completely unseaworthy vessel has to be glossed over if this theory is to be believed.)

On the other hand, supporting evidence for other details, not applying necessarily only to triremes, could be called. Taking into account the evolution of the pentecontor into two- and three-levellers, we felt justified in applying to the trireme the facts that were known about these earlier ships. Pictures of pentecontors – the single-banked fifty-oared ship – abound (they are, after all, *so* much easier to draw!) and it is reasonable to assume that the general configuration of rigging, steering, anchors and the like were similar to those on a trireme. The most eye-catching of these features is the dramatically upswept stern of all the ships. Although picturesque, this is also practical. The rocky shelving coasts of the Aegean make landing difficult, but an overhanging stern permits a ship to get close enough inshore to moor, and, as is shown on the Ruvo vase, to rig a convenient gangplank. Since triremes moored every night and at least once during the day, this was a matter of some importance.

The Greenwich debate proved to be a critical point in the history of trireme research and enabled us to add considerably to our stock of working hypotheses. The proceedings, and the conclusions reached from them, were published in *The Greek Trireme of the Fifth Century BC* (National Maritime Museum), edited by John Coates and Sean McGrail.

Some practical points emerged from working the mock-up. Although our Cambridge crew, who were trained on shells with sliding seats on the waterline and had no experience of pulling a sea boat with much steeper oar angles, soon fell into a satisfactory rhythm, they did encounter some problems.

1. The thranite (top) oar was so steeply inclined as to limit the amount of work that it could do.

2. Blades were too close together in the water, requiring an undue amount of concentration to avoid collisions.

3. The thalamian (bottom) oar handle was too high relative to the seat and too close to the beams above it.

4. Oar blades would benefit from being differently shaped on each level: the thranites' blades longer, and the thalamians' wider, to permit greater contact with the water.

This latter interesting suggestion was advanced by Sir Simon Cassels, who wrote:

> Recognizing that the shape of the oars has been largely based on contemporary drawings, it is possible that the artists and designers/decorators of pottery were not seamen. They therefore drew what they thought they saw, namely oars of a uniform shape, whereas there were subtle differences between each bank of oars. Had they drawn or decorated from personal knowledge, they would have shown the differences because these were essential to the efficient functioning of the oars in propelling the trireme.
>
> Today in Art School a student is invited to test his drawing of some artifact by asking the question 'will it work?' For example, would his drawing of a tea-pot convey to others that it would stand upright, hold liquid, keep it hot and pour it out without spilling? To my casual eye, I wonder whether the ancient Greek felt he had to be so meticulous. He had to give the correct impression but often these appear to have been stylized rather than accurate representations.

This point was well taken and the design of the oars was altered to give differently shaped blades to each rank (fig. 34). This also explained how it was possible to distinguish between the oars fitted to different levels, as the Athenian navy lists had indicated.

The crew's objections were worrying and more difficult to meet: we could never expect to attain high speeds if a whole rank was pulling at less than its capacity. But the interior space was already cramped, and putting the thranites lower down, as would have to be done if the angle of their oars was to be reduced, would restrict it even more.

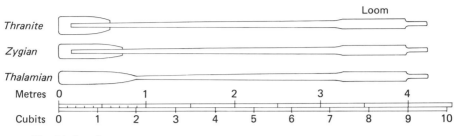

Fig. 34 Oar shapes

The middle rank, the zygians, were happy enough; they were sitting where the crew of the original pentecontor would have been, on the thwarts, and their oars were in the natural position. The lot of the thalamians, those who got farted upon in the bottom rank, was less pleasant. In their dark, foetid and cramped quarters they at least had the consolation of an easy rowing position, more akin to that of a modern skiff. Their proximity to the waterline limited the height at which their seats could be set; just as the thranites had to be low enough to give a reasonably easy angle, the thalamians had to be high enough above the water to be able to row at all.

If it were however possible to squeeze the ranks nearer together, the rewards would be great. Not only would we get better performance from our oarsmen, but the freeboard (the height of the ship above the waterline) would be decreased, and this in turn would have favourable consequences for the centre of gravity and the metacentric height. Mr Sleeswyck had been right to be concerned about this, even if his proposed solution had to be ruled out on other grounds.

John Coates's solution was ingenious. He simply canted the thranite and thalamian seats inboard, putting the thranite stretchers (foot rests) into the empty space between the zygians, thus enabling their seats to be lowered, and juggled a bit with the thole-pins. The thranite oars then sloped at $32\frac{1}{2}°$ rather than $37°$; oar blades were one and a half times further apart; and the freeboard was lowered by 0.20 m (8 "). This was fine for the thranites, and satisfactorily reduced the metacentric height, making for a more stable vessel. The problem of the thalamians remained one that correspondents to *The Times* had expressed. Could a practicable ship really have so many holes cut so near the waterline? Should it not be essential to have them higher in the hull? Only sea trials can finally provide an

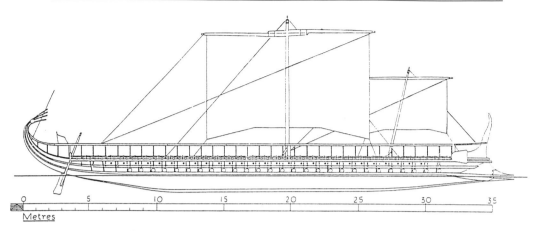

Fig. 35 John Coates's reconstruction of the trireme

answer, but some other factors encouraged us to keep the thalamians where we had put them, and are discussed in the next section.

One of the participants at the conference, Professor Thomas Gillmer, a veteran American scholar of wooden-boat building, argued eloquently for the merits of the rocker keel, and produced a drawing showing an elegantly curved hull which incorporated the beautiful carving from Lindos on Rhodes, showing the upswept stern of a ship – although not of a trireme. There were two powerful arguments against this. First, a continuously curved keel would complicate the whole geometry of the hull, not only making slipping more difficult but complicating construction. Every oar position would have to differ slightly, but crucially, from the next. When one considers that triremes were built extremely quickly and in great numbers (200 were built by Athens alone in the year before Salamis), simplicity of production was clearly essential. And of course, we would be back in the position of having some of the thranites too high up to be able to row properly.

After a good deal of consideration we decided that a straight keel was essential, although the original design was altered to be rather shorter in the central section, with lengthened cut-aways at either end, and a pronounced kick-up towards the stern. The parallel middle body was retained, and the wetted surface below the waterline reduced. These alterations all tended to make a faster and stronger ship, the 'giant arrow', of which the head would be a scaled down version of the Atlit ram (fig. 32).

The profile of our ship could now be regarded as fixed: with straight keel, low freeboard, projecting bronze ram and shapely unswept stern, she looked every inch an elegant killer (fig. 35). More complex and mundane questions remained to be settled before we would know whether she would be capable of performing as well as she looked.

The keel is, as we have said, the backbone of a ship, and Dick Steffy did not approve of our first thoughts on the matter. He felt the section we had used was incorrect: 'Ancient keels were keystone shaped for a very important reason – simplicity of construction.' He was able to prove this from the evidence of the wrecks he had examined. The keel section is important because the whole underwater shape of a wooden ship is determined by the angle at which the planks and ribs fit into the keel. A flat-bottomed boat, such as a Thames barge, has the planking meeting the keel at right angles; an old fashioned racing yacht has the planking shooting up at a steep angle, giving a sharply sloping hull.

Dick Steffy made it clear that the trireme should have an underwater section shaped like a wineglass, or an inverted late medieval church window (fig. 36). In a modern ship this would be easy enough: the ship's skeleton is formed by ribs, aptly so named, projecting from the keel. These can be curved to any required shape, and the planks are simply nailed to them. But ancient methods of ship construction, with the planks firmly joined to each other on both sides for the whole of their length, posed problems.

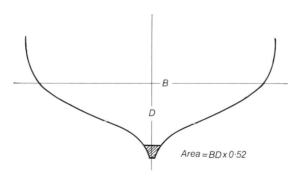

Fig. 36 The wineglass-shaped hull section, as used in the Punic ship of Marsala, 300–200 BC

Commander Eric McKee, who was advising the Trust on methods of wooden-boat building, had worked on many North European projects including the Graveney boat reconstruction, the Gokstad faering, and a Somerset Levels pcat boat. Like Steffy, but working in a different discipline and tradition, he was able to make deductions based on the practical limitations of wooden construction, as palaeontologists can recreate an entire animal from a single bone.

Eric pointed out that the accepted method of joining planks edge to edge imposed a vital restriction on the hull profile. Planks could only be jointed together at a slight angle; if a sharp angle were attempted the tenon peg would be driven so near the skin of the plank as to weaken it dangerously (fig. 37). He calculated that an angle of 20° between planks was

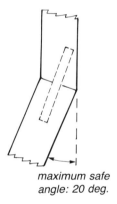

maximum safe angle: 20 deg.   Fig. 37 *Joining the planks edge to edge: the safe angle*

the maximum that could safely be allowed. But if Steffy's clear opinions on the hull shape were to be heeded, as they must, much sharper angles than 20° had to be accommodated. And indeed, in the ancient wrecks, so they were. This was managed by carving the planks nearest to the keels from thicker baulks of wood, and building the curve into the planks themselves, rather than the joints. The process of carving is of course both arduous and time-consuming, and was only done on those planks where it was essential; other, higher, planks conformed to the McKee formula.

Designing a hull that fitted these requirements, in addition to the other parameters, narrowed even further the range of possible solutions, but it all worked out perfectly. The carved planks next to the keel contributed to the strength of the keel itself, like the well-developed muscles of an athlete reinforcing the strength of the spine, while the gentle curves of the remainder gave a light and buoyant ogival shape to the whole. But the unhappy thalamians remained inescapably confined to their original positions.

The definition of the wineglass/church window section was more fundamental than might appear. All previous investigators had seen ancient ships in the light of what was familiar to them: Renaissance writers saw the trireme as a sixteenth-century galley and nineteenth-century commentators thought in terms of a contemporary sailing-ship with a U-shaped hull section. Dupuy de Lôme's trireme, which had failed to perform under oar, would probably have coped well enough with Channel breezes. Even more up-to-date and better informed reconstructions fell into the same trap: Foley, Soedel, and Sleeswyck all adopted the U-shaped hull.

But given the historical restrictions, the three-tier system simply will not work in a hull of that shape. Only with the sharply flared hull we adopted could the 170 oarsmen, all with equal-length oars, be accommodated. And, as Dr Tarn pointed out more than fifty years ago, the trireme is a racing machine, which it could never have been with a full U-shaped hull.

There was an interesting side-effect to this. The ogival shape meant that the thalamians were seated some way inboard, from which it followed that their thole-pins must be inboard as well: the distance between the man and the pivot has to be constant. If the pivot is inside the hull the oar must travel a fair way within the hull itself: ergo, there must be a biggish hole to enable it to do so. When we finally got the positions right, and calculated the size of the hole, it was exactly the right size to stick a man's head through, as was done to the unfortunate Scylax. Archaeology, history, and mechanics had all combined to give the same answer, which was a comforting thought.

All these alterations, prompted by observations of practical oarsmen, experienced sailors, boat-builders and archaeologists, were incorporated in revised drawings. We were very pleased indeed, for it confirmed that we were on the right track, that these alterations made our ship look even more like the Lenormant relief, and also had the effect of improving her seakeeping qualities. No insuperable objections had been raised, and a communal sigh of relief was heard as we considered what might be done next.

Like our first press conference, the Greenwich symposium attracted international coverage. *The Times* reported that 'yesterday's trial, on the first day of a two-day conference to discuss the project, finally discredited suggestions that the top (thranite) file must have had longer oars or rowed standing up'. Television companies were delighted by the sight of grown men splashing about in bits of boats; modest offers of financial support began to appear; and it seemed that we might seriously begin to contemplate a building programme.

'All there is to say about ship timbers'

W E had now to emerge from the engaging business of playing about in paddling pools under the amused eyes of television cameramen and address ourselves seriously to the problem of a reconstruction. That was the term that we agreed should be used; we could not very convincingly call our ship a replica, since there were so many unknown factors where we had nothing but inspired guess-work on which to rely.

There would be many hazards ahead, for just as the design had needed years of skilled analysis, the building itself would involve techniques that had not been employed for over a millenium. No yard could be expected to master these without detailed guidance.

John Coates pointed out firmly that an essential first step must therefore be to build a 'trial piece'. This would be a section through the ship to be constructed of the same materials and using the same methods that we would employ in the completed ship, and to the same scale. Superficially the trial piece would resemble the mock-up, but the latter had been designed only to demonstrate the oar system, and had been cobbled together out of any materials that came to hand. The trial piece would, by contrast, have to be very carefully built in the most authentic way possible. John had in mind a section that would be about one-fifth of one side, or a tenth of the whole. As a one-off project, and an experimental one at that, the trial piece might be expected to be proportionately more expensive than the whole ship would be, but it would at least give a guide to costs; even a straight-forward multiplication by ten would be a sight more accurate than my first uninstructed guess. But before we could begin work on the trial piece there were other points that needed to be settled. What timbers, for example, should we use?

We know a good deal about the sort of woods the Greeks used in ship-building, thanks mainly to Theophrastos, an engaging writer, a pupil of and successor to Aristotle. Theophrastos wrote a book of 'characters', a collection of types still very much recognizable. There is, for example, Complaisant Man:

> At a dinner party he asks his host to have the children brought in, and when they make an appearance he calls them the very image of their father . . . He gets his hair cut all the time, too, and keeps his teeth painfully white. More than that, he changes his linen while it is still perfectly clean and he uses scented lotions. Downtown you can find him in the banking section . . .

More relevantly to our purposes, Theophrastos also wrote about timber:

> Fir, mountain pine, and cedar are the standard ship-timbers. Triremes and long ships [i.e. other warships] are made of fir because it is light, while round ships [merchantmen] are made of pine because it does not decay. Some people, however, make their triremes of pine also, because they have no adequate supply of fir. These woods are used for the main timbers, but for the trireme's keel oak is used because it has to stand up to hauling . . . They make the cutwater and catheads, which require special strength, of ash, mulberry, or elm.

Fir is a mountain tree, less plentiful in the Mediterranean than pine. Silver fir, which was found only in Macedonia, was held in highest repute among the Greeks. Tim Severin had used Aleppo pine (*Pinus brutia*) for the *Argo*, but this wood, although quite satisfactory for merchantmen as Theophrastos pointed out, was not ideal for a trireme.

Theophrastos also suggested that we should use less than fully seasoned wood for planking, in order to make bending easier, but not for the tenons, which had to be cut from the strongest available timber.

After consultation with the Building Research Establishment it was decided to use Douglas fir, otherwise known as Oregon pine, for the planks, as being the nearest equivalent to either Silver fir or Mediterranean pine. True firs would certainly be light enough, but would be too short-lived for a ship we hoped would be maintained in a seaworthy condition for some years.

It would be difficult to the point of impossibility to find seasoned straight-grained oak for the keel, and lamination was both inauthentic and expensive, so we adopted iroko for that and for the ram timbers. We had also to address ourselves as well to the question of how the all-important joints that held the planks together edge to edge were made. The light hull would depend for its strength on the planking, and we had to get this right. But here we came up against the difficulty that no fragment of a trireme hull existed to give any detailed guidance as to how to go about it.

A number of passages in literature underlined the importance of these joints. When, for example, Odysseus was caught out in a storm after leaving Calypso in the ship he had himself built, he was confident that 'as long as the planks are held fast in the mortice and tenon joints, so long will I stay aboard and suffer the worst that comes'.

The Kyrenia ship was not much help in deciding how we should proceed, since the stresses that would be felt in that slow and heavy hull were much less than we might expect in ours. The mortice and tenon joints in her planking were 150 mm apart and only 6 mm thick, far too widely spaced and slight for a warship. The later Carthaginian warship found by Honor Frost was more nearly akin to our vessel, although smaller and less singlemindedly built for speed. Her joints, for example, were 90 mm apart and 9 mm thick.

In order to discover what would be needed for the trireme, we had to resort to experiment. Using the Carthaginian ship as a starting point, Norman Gundry, a retired naval constructor with practical experience in wooden boats and another of John Coates's many friends, carried out some shear tests on replicas of the joints found in the Marsala ship. Although they were subjected to only half the stresses we expected in the trireme, they failed absolutely — 'as though some one had tried to cut them in half with a gigantic pair of blunt shears', John commented.

It looked remarkably as if the trireme was, as we had always suspected, a ship built to the limits of the available technology, and not to be compared with any other known vessel. John decided to step up the thickness of the tenons to 12 mm, well beyond the relative size of any found in wrecks, to use the hardest oak that we could lay our hands on, and to beef up the size of the holding pegs by 50 per cent. This would give us an immensely strong shell, but would need a great deal of high precision joinery: 40,000 mortices to be cut and pegs driven, all precisely. And, as Eric McKee had proved, there could be no increase in the plank curvature.

111

The invaluable Theophrastos was a trifle vague as to the wood we should use for the joints: 'In merchant ships the internal woodwork is made of mulberry or ash or elm or plane since it must be cheap and tough . . . Sometimes the internal parts of triremes are made of coastal pine as well, because of its light weight.' He ends dismissively: 'This is about all there is to say about ship-timbers.' However both the Atlit ram timbers and the Kyrenia ship were joined together with oak tenons, and that was what we used. Northern European oak is too soft for such strenuous work, and we used American live oak (*Quercus Virginiana*) very generously given to us by one of our American supporters, Leon Neel of Georgia.

John also believed it necessary to have a computer test of his hull lines. By any normal ship-building standards the trireme had to be regarded as an extreme design. The ratio of her waterline length to breadth was 9:1 and that of length to depth below the waterline more than 10:1. In the days of wooden-ship building, even of clippers, eyebrows would have been raised at such proportions, and any ship following them would be regarded as unseaworthy.

In fact a ship so constructed would be unlikely even to survive its own launch unless it were given some reinforcement. In order to hold together a hull so long, shallow, narrow, and light, something more was needed. That something was the mysterious object known as the hypozoma (pl. hypozomata), usually, but misleadingly, translated as undergirdle. Exactly what this might have been was far from clear. Certainly it was a rope, and a most important one. Every ship was required to carry four, and they appeared first on the list of a ship's equipment. Without them a trireme could not be regarded as commissioned, and if a long voyage were planned spares were carried. Like pitch and sailcloth, they were classed as contraband of war. Their weight was recorded; one hypozoma weighed about 250 lbs, and was therefore about 280' to 340' long; more than enough to encircle a 120' ship. It was plaited or twisted; one regulation prescribes the number of men who had to be employed in fitting it. The tension that this imparted gradually declined, necessitating re-tightening during the voyage. And, just to confuse matters more, there is one reference to the hypozoma of a battering ram.

Whatever it may have been, the hypozoma was well enough known to be used as a simile by Plato. In the *Laws* Plato compares the hypozomata to the tendons of the human body; in *The Republic* he talks poetically about a bond of light holding the heavens together like the hypozomata of triremes. Apollonius of Rhodes, who wrote down the story of the Argonauts, described how the first thing they did with their ship was to fit a hypozoma, girdling 'the ship strongly with a well-twisted rope from within, putting a tension on each extremity, so that the planks should fit well together with the dowels and withstand the opposing force of the sea'.

A 'girdle' sounds very much as if it were something wrapped around the ship like a piece of string tying a parcel together, and in *Greek Oared Ships* John Morrison tentatively reached that conclusion: John Coates, however, on starting his design, could not see that a rope placed in such a way served any useful purpose. If it was so important to the safety of the ship, the hypozoma must be an integral part of the design, rather than something added just to make sure.

As had happened before, in default of any evidence we considered what the laws of mechanics would seem to indicate was needed.

Any ship can be described as essentially a tube that floats. If it floats at rest on a dead-still surface the water pressure is constant and creates no strains. But once it starts to move these stresses start. Even if the water remains calm, the moving vessel immediately creates its own waves, one at the front, and one following some way towards the stern. As soon as this occurs the water that has been supporting the ship between these waves starts to disappear: if the ship is going fast enough all that water may be displaced, leaving the vessel supported only by the waves (fig. 38).

Great stresses are therefore placed on the hull, causing it to droop in the middle (sagging). All ships do this, and anyone who has sailed in a

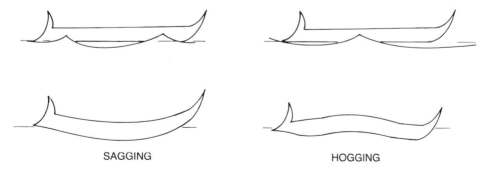

SAGGING   HOGGING

Fig. 38 Stresses caused by waves

wooden ship knows the ceaseless groanings that go on as the timbers constantly flex in response to the pressures.

When not in a dead calm, a ship also encounters natural waves, and something else happens. As these waves pass under the hull, so the support points move. If the waves are long enough the time comes when the ship is balanced on the top of one, somewhere about its middle. It then drops at both ends, a phenomenon known as 'hogging'.

These uncomfortable facts have been known since the earliest times, and ships have been made strong enough to accommodate them. But our trireme was built above all for speed, and was only expected to cope with quite modest seas. A long light tube bends more easily than a short heavy one, and to aggravate its bendability the trireme is a very shallow boat. A merchantman needs a deep hull to carry its cargo, but the trireme is a skimmer, designed to scuttle across the surface of the water causing minimum resistance.

Depth of hull is so vital a factor in strength that Lloyds of London laid down standards governing the ratio of depth to length. The trireme lies well outside these limits, and would never have gained Lloyds' approval even if it were built in the same way as were nineteenth-century ships, which of course it was not, being very much lighter. According to the best estimates, the trireme, faced with a wave equivalent to its own length and one-fortieth of that in height (which is not anything too much out-of-the-way), would be 50 per cent overloaded.

Matters were made worse by the fact that although she has a very similar length to ships of substantial size – she is longer, for example, than Captain Cook's *Endeavour* – the trireme is nothing more nor less than a large open boat. Drawings of the finished trireme are somewhat misleading, giving as they do the impression of being decked. In fact the covering is a mere canopy which contributes nothing to the structual strength of the hull. It is made in sections, to allow movement independent of the hull, and can easily be removed. Later triremes, quinqueremes and the like were properly decked, but all the strength of our trireme's hull depended on the edge-to-edge jointing of the planks, and on the hypozoma – whatever that was.

Since there would be no point in its being what we would think of as a 'girdle' round the outside of the ship, John Coates came to the conclusion that the hypozoma was a different sort of foundation garment, an anti-hogging truss. This is a common enough device in light ancient ships, and can be seen clearly in pictures of Egyptian vessels. Its function is to pull

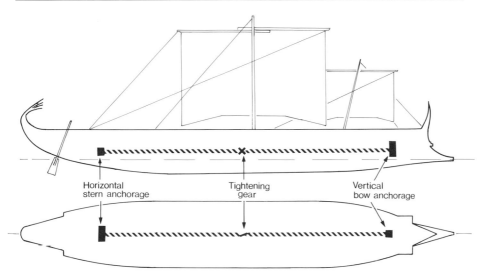

Fig. 39 Position of the hypozoma

the extremities of the hull together, making the whole very much like a gigantic bow, with the hypozoma acting as the bowstring. Even modern ships can make use of similar devices. Sailing barges, whose hulls undergo considerable strains, sometimes pass a stout rope from stem to stern, which they call a 'swifter'. As well as being a sound design requirement, this fits in with the literary evidence – Apollonius's reference to the rope being 'from within'; and some obscure references both in Plato and in later inscriptions to the hypozoma having 'braces', which a device of this sort would need (fig. 39).

The final design has two parallel ropes, each looped round anchorages firmly fixed at either end of the ship. The ropes run down the middle line, between the files of oarsmen, and just below the main beam level. Tension is put on the ropes by a device placed amidships, in which a bar is used to twist them, at first directly by hand and then, as the tension increases, by using levers pulled round by hauling tackle. It is exactly the same principle as that used by small boys in flying elastic-powered model aeroplanes. Unlike model-aeroplane elastic, the trireme's ropes can be re-tightened at sea.

This simple but effective method was devised by another of John Coates's friend, a retired naval engineer officer. Rear Admiral Dorian Dymoke's service experience had included designing aircraft catapults, so it was highly suitable that he should turn his hand to another engineering project with boyish associations.

Some objections have been raised to our approach to this and similar problems. The purist can claim, with some justification, that such proposals are purely conjectural; there is no evidence at all that the hypozoma functioned as John Coates and Dorian Dymoke have suggested.

The response to this is that the principles of engineering do not change; the limits of the possible are the same now as they were in the fifth century BC, and it was encouraging to see how often the solution to one difficulty corroborated another theory. That ocurred with the considerations of hull stress.

While John Coates was first working out what stresses the trireme might encounter in the seas it could be expected to meet, he discovered that the worst conditions might develop before it was even launched. The ancient sheds slope, naturally enough, towards the water, just as does a modern slipway: a slope of 1:10 seems to be typical. When the vessel slides from its slip into the sea the forward section, taking the water first, bobs up and floats while the after part of the ship is still on dry land. In doing this the weight of the vessel hinges on a small section of the keel, giving rise to severe sagging stresses. Our original design, based upon the Marsala ship, had a long keel with a sharp upturn towards the stern. This might not have incommoded the Marsala vessel on launching, since her hull was shorter, but the longer trireme would have an unacceptable load placed upon its keel. This load would be greater than that imposed by the sort of seas that might be expected, and might be quite enough to split the ship before it left the shed.

John Coates had already found other reasons for concern about the length of our keel. The originally designed long straight keel would make beaching inconvenient and militate against the ability to make sharp turns that was so important in trireme tactics. If the keel were made shorter, with a longer swing up to the stern, we would gain these points and, much more importantly, reduce the severe stresses on launching. Moving the after cut up forward by a distance equal to one-tenth of the waterline length would reduce the sagging stress by one-half.

This was all satisfactorily coherent; the dimensions of the sheds, the practicability of oar operation, the restrictions imposed by the methods of construction, and the demand for a high-speed craft inexorably dictated the design. Nevertheless, in order to make quite certain, the plans were submitted to some theoretical tests, essentially the same as those carried out when designing a modern ship. The Wolfson Marine Research Unit at Southampton did a computer study to check John Coates's calculations and confirmed that these were correct, and that the ship could cope with the stresses that we expected in service.

The University of Athens, under the direction of Professor Theodore Loukakis, prepared a model for tank tests, which also proved satisfactory. In fact, the tests indicated that the theoretical maximum speed we might expect from the hull was over 10 knots, which would enable our trireme to match the speeds recorded in classical times, and confound the doubters.

While John Coates was contemplating the workload that building even one-tenth of the ship involved, and setting up the experiments, John Morrison and I were exploring the possibility of starting the actual construction. Not that we had any money to do so, but the decision to build a trial piece inevitably raised in its train the question of progressing to the final ship. Certainly any yard that had mastered the complexities of ancient shipbuilding in the course of working on the trial piece would be well placed to follow it with the whole ship, if money could be found.

It seemed imperative that the trial piece at any rate should be built in an English yard, preferably one within easy reach of John Coates's home at Bath, where he could be permanently at hand to extract bugs and iron out wrinkles. But when we came to consider the total reconstruction we found ourselves on the horns of a dilemma, always an uncomfortable place.

It would be much more convenient to build the entire ship in England, where we could keep a constant eye on things, deal with problems as they cropped up, and make any alteration that would be necessary. On the other hand, if we did this, what could we do with the finished ship?

Triremes, as has been said, only ever operated in calm and sheltered water; even a modest chop, which might not be absolutely dangerous, would drastically impede her performance. She could only be rowed in England with any degree of safety on lakes and rivers, and not many of those.

Worse, there was the heavy hand of bureaucracy. Department of Trade regulations governing the operation of passenger boats are as manifold as they are illogical. They allow such floating death-traps as car ferries to operate with the most primitive of safety devices, and make no attempt to test the skills of thousands of small-boat sailors who risk their lives every summer, but place the most pettifogging restrictions on anything slightly out of the ordinary.

Without much doubt they would insist on lifejackets, rafts, flares, and such like paraphernalia for which room could never be found, and would demand qualified skippers – though who could be properly qualified to operate a ship that had not seen the light of day for 1,500 years? Nor could insurers be expected to be anxious to provide cover for the ship or her 200 crew. And for our part, common prudence would dictate that we should have suitable tenders and emergency boats constantly available.

In short, although it would be convenient to build the ship in England, we could never hope to sail it there, but would have to ship it out to more suitable waters. To do this would necessitate building a cradle in which the ship could travel, and the extra cost would be almost equivalent to the whole cost of building, to say nothing of the expense of shipment.

On the other hand, if we were to build in Greece, the problems of communication and supervision would demand more resources than we could spare. At the minimum, John Coates, an interpreter and a master-builder would need to be permanently there, adding to the expense. The legal problems of managing a complex contract under Greek law would constitute another difficulty.

We had no money for either course of action, but were determined not to let this stand in our way. Something, we felt, was sure to turn up.

Liverpool, Edwin Wolff's city, seemed a reasonable place to start looking. As part of Michael Heseltine's initiative, a trust had been founded there in order to build a replica of a Mersey pilot cutter. It would be very convenient if the skills of the young people who had been trained on that boat could be applied, when they had finished, to ours. The timing would be suitable, and the Manchester Ship Canal or the Weaver Navigation both offered potential testing waters. Liverpool was planning an extensive maritime museum in the Albert Docks, which would make a permanent home for the trireme. We were exploring the possibility of building in Liverpool when, very properly for so classical a project, the Fates took a hand, and directed our attention to Greece.

Greece is at once the youngest and oldest of European nations. Though it has a history and a language going back more than 4,000 years, the Greek State only took its present form in 1947 when the islands of the Dodecanese were restored. The Greeks have had to fight many times since independence; in the present century against Germans, Italians, Turks and Bulgarians as well as in a damaging civil war. Perhaps for that reason our idea of reconstructing a trireme, an example of the most glorious days of Greek history, struck a sympathetic chord.

And the day of Salamis was probably the most glorious in that long history. It should, looking at matters realistically, have marked the end of Greek independence and the absorption of all Greeks in the Persian empire. As the eventual inheritors of the Assyrians, the Persians had consolidated their dominions rapidly. Within a few years of the accession of the first Persian monarch, Cyrus, their empire had spread from the Mediterranean to the Indian Ocean, including what is now Turkey, Persia, Iraq, the Levant, Arabia, Egypt, Afghanistan and much of Pakistan. Previously independent states were often allowed to retain nominal independence, but were left in no doubt whose lead they were to follow.

Though rebellions were put down with a firmness that usually included large-scale dismemberment and impalement, they did not entirely cease. Those Ionian Greek states on the coast of Asia Minor that had been absorbed into the empire were particularly prone to restiveness, and were able to call for help from the Greeks on the other side of the Aegean who had so far escaped Persian domination.

One of these Ionian rebellions was joined by an Athenian expeditionary force, which succeeded in carrying the war into the Persian camp by sacking the royal city of Sardis. Darius, the Persian monarch, took this as a personal insult, and formally swore vengeance on the impertinent Athenians. Drawing upon the whole might of his extensive dominions, Darius mounted a huge invasion of mainland Greece and quickly reached the borders of Attica.

Even 2,500 years later Western consciousness still responds to the resistance that the tiny Greek states advanced in the face of Persian power. The 'Star Wars' films, with their Evil Empire imagery, are nothing more than a replay of that ancient story. The contrast was real enough. Not all of the free Greek states were democracies, or anything remotely resembling them, but all had traditions of free debate and discussion, often indeed carried to tiresome extremes: and no Greek of that time would have dreamed of equating a king with a god, as was common in the East. Absolutism was complete in the Persian Empire, as it had been in the Assyrian. A whim of the Great King could move armies or destroy provinces; Greeks demanded a full-scale debate before deciding any matter, and were quite capable of going off in a huff if the decision did not suit them.

Darius's army was halted by the great battle of Marathon, where Athenians and Spartans fought side by side under the command of Miltiades. Frustrated and furious, Darius died, but his successor Xerxes took upon himself the fulfilment of Darius' oath, and set about preparing for the final obliteration of the Athenians.

All the resources of the Persian empire were mobilized to crush the presumptuous Athenians and their allies. According to Herodotus, 1,700,000 men – Medes and Persians, accompanied by Scythians, Indians, Bactrians, Arabians, Ethiopians, Libyans, and Greeks from the subject Asian cities – marched across the bridge of boats Xerxes had built over the Hellespont. Twelve hundred and seven triremes accompanied the army in order to safeguard its lines of communication. When a natural object threatened the inexorable progress of the invasion it was dealt with; a canal was dug through the Mount Athos peninsula in order to avoid rounding the dangerous cape. This enormous and seemingly invincible force was stopped in its tracks by the triremes at Salamis.

If this had not happened history would have been changed drastically. The great lurch forward that humanity made in the century or so after 480 BC was concentrated almost exclusively in Athens, a small, divided and quarrelsome city state, its inhabitants ebullient with enthusiasm at having defeated the greatest power in the world. It is difficult to believe that the same genius would have found expression under the absolute power of the satrap of Attica and the Peloponnese. In fifth-century Athens, art, architecture, literature, science, language, philosophy and politics made either great advances or indeed a virtual start. And, unlike similar phenomena in other civilizations which later succumbed to external pressures, such as the Aztec and Egyptian, Greek achievements were secured, encapsulated for centuries in a society which became stable enough to enable them to be transmitted from generation to generation. In spite of destruction, war and the passage of time, European civilization has retained at its core the Greek experience.

Sceptical modernists may claim that what went on in fifth-century Athens is irrelevant to late-twentieth-century problems. In recent years the world has become a smaller place and we are rightly more conscious of cultural traditions other than the Graeco-Roman-Judaic mix of Western

Europe. The art, music and philosophy of China and India are beginning to be properly appreciated, to the extent that modish enthusiasts now dismiss classic European culture. The cool logic that forms the greatest Greek strength is scorned, as religious fundamentalists of many faiths flout rational argument and demand – sometimes by force – acquiescence in their own superstitions.

But the Greek tradition, even when neglected, is very much more pervasive than is sometimes realized. We owe to Greece the very concepts and terms we use to defend our particular values, however disparate these may be, to attack those we dislike and to undertake our more important activities. Scientific investigation is a Greek invention; the concepts behind 'nuclear' and 'physics' were first expressed by the Greeks; democracy, oligarchy, autocracy and self-sufficiency were analysed by them; justification for communism, fascism, imperialism, colonialism – or their antitheses – can be found in Greek writings. And the inheritors of these ideas are now as much Indian, Chinese, African or Polynesian as European. The Roman, Spanish, Dutch, French and Russian empires have acted as carriers of Greek ideas; the spread of the English language has rendered them universally accessible.

Looking back, all this sounds like an inevitable progression, but there was nothing inevitable about it at the time. The achievements of fifth-century Greece might survive today only as antiquarian curiosities, like those of the Mayan or Sumerian empires, or have stagnated for millennia in self-absorbed satisfaction, as with the Han dynasties. Christianity and Islam might have become the religions of tiny communities, like Zoroastrianism, or have fizzled out unremarked like the cults of Isis or Mithras; the *Iliad* and the *Odyssey* might, like the epic of Gilgamesh, be sterile objects of interest to a few specialist scholars.

But even so, the works of the fifth-century Greeks are only patchily accessible. Very few of us can appreciate the literature except in translation; their music is entirely lost; their paintings largely so; their science has become absorbed in the corpus of scientific learning. To those raised on Western European Gothic, even the best preserved temples look a little dull. Only the ceramics and statuary speak clearly and directly to the ordinary twentieth-century observer.

The peculiar interest of the trireme is therefore three-fold; it is first a complex and ingenious artifact, and its reconstruction enables the high degree of technical skills available to fifth-century Athens to be understood for the first time. We can all appreciate the mechanical ingenuity that must then have been commonplace, and the energy and flexibility of a society that enabled so many ships to be produced so quickly.

Secondly, the ship itself was absolutely central to Athenian consciousness and to the development of Athenian hegemony. It had been the instrument of the Persian defeat: a proud Athenian described himself as coming 'from the city where they build fine triremes'. On Delos a temple built in order to house the sacred trireme that brought the yearly tribute from Athens can still be seen. Being able to see, and even better being able to row in, a trireme capable of making passages almost as quickly as a small ferry, would demonstrate strikingly how Athenian power had been spread.

Finally, the trireme really was a remarkably elegant ship: with the sailing clipper, perhaps the most beautiful of vessels ever to take to the water. And John Coates's design, as agreed at the Greenwich conference, was clearly going to result in a magnificent ship.

The first intimations of serious Greek interest in helping with the project came in September 1983, when, following our Greenwich conference, John Coates and Eric McKee were invited to inspect the beginnings of work on the Kyrenia ship reconstruction. They were received by the enormously hospitable Tzalas and Tzamtzis, and shown all the local relics – sheds, harbours, the Themistoclean Walls, and the famous eyes in the Piraeus museum, as well as the yard where the Kyrenia's keel was to be laid. As some modest return, John gave a lecture at the Hellenic Maritime Museum on our project. This proved very successful. Among his audience were some officers of the Greek Navy, who had been independently studying the trireme and had come to very much the same conclusions about the oar systems that we had done. They were greatly taken with the idea of attempting a reconstruction, and asked John and Eric to attend a hastily convened meeting the next day at General Headquarters, Athens.

This was very much the right element for John Coates and Eric McKee. John, as an experienced naval architect, was talking to the men who sailed in the ships he had designed. Eric was himself a retired naval officer able to speak with authority on wooden-ship and -boat building techniques. Both men were professionals addressing fellow professionals on matters of common and enthusiastic interest.

The senior of those present was Commodore Ioannis Kolliniatis, in charge of naval dockyards and a man of considerable presence, who had already made up his mind that we were on the right track but felt strongly that the ship should be built in Greece. If this were done, he offered, the Greek Navy would take the ship under its wing, operate and preserve it.

Such an offer was important, for wooden ships, especially if of so light a construction and specialist nature as a trireme, are difficult and expensive to maintain. It did not, however, help with our major concern, which was finding the cash with which to build it, and John politely expressed this view, while much appreciating the generosity of the proposal.

Government departments are not famous for quick reactions, but three days later the Commodore was back. The Hellenic Navy would not only look after the ship on completion, but would supervise construction under our guidance, and, together with other Greek institutions, would find half the cost.

This was a serious offer, subsequently confirmed in a letter to me from Admiral Makris and Captain Tzamtzis, and one made by a first-rate organization: the efficiency of the Hellenic Navy is proverbial in Greece, and it is held in the highest respect not only in Greece but among the other NATO forces.

When John Coates came back with his news we were presented with a challenge. We had no problems in agreeing to the Navy's proposal: it was entirely appropriate that the ship should be built in Greece, and the difficulties we had foreseen in controlling the work so far from home would be much lessened by the Navy's supervision. We would not have to concern ourselves with day-to-day management or complex legalities. And of course there was no doubt in our minds that Greek waters were the right place for that essentially Greek ship. It was only an historic accident that the initiative and research had come from England. But there remained the problem of producing our share of the construction costs, which on my original estimate would amount to £125,000, as well as the balance of research and development, making the whole sum about £200,000. If we were to be able to take advantage of the Navy's handsome offer we would need to move rapidly.

The *Daily Express* had invited us to demonstrate the mock-up at the 1984 Boat Show, which gave us the opportunity of free publicity and the chance to raise our part of the building costs. The show enabled us to test the mock-up in a more capacious tank, and with thousands of volunteer oarsmen. It worked well from the point of view of publicity: every day weary pin-stripe-suited and sombre men left their umbrellas in the corner of our stand, took off their jackets, rolled up their sleeves and clambered on to the boat section for a vigorous twenty-minute rowing exercise. It took only a few minutes for these scratch crews to fall into a powerful and effective rhythm. Indeed, strict supervision had to be exercised to avoid flooding Earls Court.

As a fund-raising exercise, though, it was less successful. On the last night two small children stripped off and dived into the pool to collect the donations we had received, which came closer to £1,000 than the £200,000 we were looking for. However it was all great fun, if slightly damp, and kept us busy till February 1984, when John Morrison and I went out to Athens to talk over the Navy's proposals. We took the opportunity, guided by Admiral Makris and Captain Tzamtzis, of looking at the island of Poros, which had impressed me on my first visit as being an ideal location for sea trials. Even in classical times, when trireme builders presumably knew what they were doing and crews were experienced, the ships only put to sea in favourable conditions, as we have seen, and then stayed close to the coasts. If we succeeded in getting the trireme built it would incorporate many hypotheses and reservations, and be crewed by oarsmen who had never handled anything similar. In those circumstances, a park lake on a still summer's day could be dangerous.

We would certainly not stray far from land, and would be accompanied by rescue boats, but we did not want to be too restricted by weather conditions. Trial crews would only be got together – 170-plus trained oarsmen are not easy to come by – for limited periods, and would not want to waste time hanging about waiting for a dead calm.

The island of Poros is an agreeable and accessible spot, which can be reached by ferry or hydrofoil from Piraeus, some forty miles to the north, or by road through Corinth, Epidauros and Troezen. An enthusiastic tourist can make an informative round trip, taking in Mycenae, Tiryns, and Aegina as well, before collapsing into the fleshpots of Piraeus. The island is separated from the mainland by a sheltered lagoon-like strait, which gives a four-mile stretch of water that is safe in almost all weather conditions (fig. 40). Poros, we agreed, was admirable. It would have to be a very bad day for operations to be impossible there, should we ever get as far as actually having a trireme to row, which was now assuming a degree of possibility.

We met in the combined services HQ in Athens, and the Navy's proposal was clearly set out. They would carry out the whole construction from

Fig. 40 The straits off Poros

seeking tenders, through to supervising building, launching, testing, producing a deck crew and support vessels for the maiden voyage, and permanent care of the ship. For their part, the Trust would provide full working drawings and specifications, would complete the trial piece, give guidance on building, and have the use of the ship for sea trials. Each party would pay half the cost of construction.

The Navy wanted to press ahead, starting work that year when the money would be available in their budgets. They would therefore need a firm commitment from us to put up our half of the cash at that time.

This was not a promise we could properly give. The most that we could say was that we would do our best, and felt reasonably confident that given time, the money could be found. At any rate we would undertake to press ahead at all speed with drawings and complete the trial piece, which would enable competitive tenders from the boatyards to be sought, at the same time scurrying about to see whether we could raise our share of the money. The Greek Navy very decently agreed to leave their offer open while we had a chance to look for support.

Before returning to England John Morrison and I were also invited to cast our inexpert eyes over the Psaros yard at Perama where the Kyrenia ship reconstruction had started.

Although that sailing merchant ship was quite unlike the trireme, the two ships would have much in common. It was difficult to believe that different techniques could have been used to build two such contemporary ships, even if they were hardly similar in purpose. Just as a modern yard can switch from building freighters to warships, employing the same men and machinery, so did the fifth-century Greeks move from one to the other. The sheer scale of trireme building before Salamis must have necessitated every man able to use an adze or a mallet being employed on trireme construction. And the yard would surely give us a foretaste of what conditions we might expect to account if we were to be building in Greece.

In the early days of the project we had all cherished ideas of our ships being built by sunburnt old craftsmen on some distant isle; we had heard of traditional boat-builders in Chios and Lesbos; we saw ourselves sitting in the shade, behind an ouzo, discussing the finer points of shaping the *gomphoi* with some wise and aged master-builder whose grandfather remember Lord Byron, and recreating ourselves with frequent bathes in the pellucid waters of the Aegean. The reality proved sadly otherwise.

Somewhat surprisingly, there are few Greek boat-builders still expert in wooden building: it is easier to have a traditional wooden boat constructed in high-technology America or in Britain. The Kyrenia ship was being built in one of the few yards able to undertake a wooden ship of that size. It was a disappointingly unromantic location. The Psaros yard occupies a stretch of mud in the Piraeus suburb of Perama. Rudimentary shelter is afforded by an open shed, but the mud is mostly occupied by a variety of boats, up to about 80′ in length, under repair. The view across the polluted waters to Salamis is blocked by masses of rusting shipping, laid up by the recession, and awaiting its turn at the breakers' yard.

But in spite of its unprepossessing apparance, Psaros has real craftsmen. Two were working on the keel of the Kyrenia ship – Sophocles and Byron, both swinging adzes with amazing precision, although there must have been forty years between their ages. It was very clear that both they, and the management, were confident of their ability to tackle the project. Much of Psaros's work is now repair, but they still build some fishing-boats and trehandiri-style yachts, and maintain a tradition of fine craftsmanship. Their reconstruction was going to be a simpler affair, for although the Kyrenia ship was to be a replica, using all the ancient techniques, her robust hull presented a less complex and delicate task than that which would confront whoever constructed the trireme. The builders of our ship, whoever they turned out to be, would need to watch every gram of weight and stick precisely to the drawings if 170 oarsmen were to be properly balanced.

Something of a trial

Whatever the outcome of our search for funds with which to match the Hellenic Navy's offer, it was imperative that we made progress with the trial piece. Not only was it an integral part of the design programme, but building in a Greek yard, with all the attendant difficulties of communication and distance, would be impossible without it.

We hoped at least to be able to give that part of the work to the excellent team at Liverpool, but their schedule did not allow it and we had to look elsewhere. As a charity we were bound to ask for tenders, which involved the preparation of precise working drawings and a specification. This would not be wasted effort, since the information would finally form part of the design for the ship itself.

All the trickiest details that might create difficulties in building the ship itself were included, among them the classical method of scarfing – joining the timbers of the keel together. This was by the trait-de-Jupiter (fig. 41), as complex a piece of carpentry as can be imagined, which took its name from the thunderbolt of Zeus himself.

This work all fell to John Coates, since Eric McKee had died, very suddenly, in December 1983. His death was a deeply felt loss to the project, and to naval archaeology as a whole, a loss recognized by the posthumous presentation of the first Caird medal for maritime research to be awarded.

Things were complicated by our intention to have the section rowed in water rather than merely alongside a pool. Flotation devices, which would have the effect of exactly counterbalancing that side of the hull we were building, would therefore be needed and the whole made strong enough to cope with the considerable energy that would be unleashed by fifteen

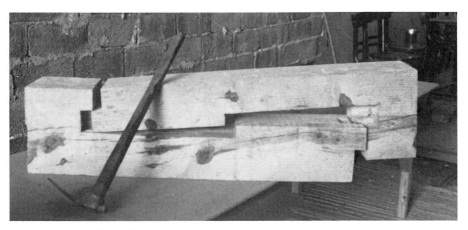

Fig. 41 Scarfing – the trait-de-Jupiter

oarsmen pulling with all their might while tethered to the quay.

It was therefore with some diffidence that we approached boatyards. 'I wonder if you would care to build one-tenth of a ship that last floated one thousand five hundred years ago, by techniques that nobody has used in that time, to an exact specification and precise dimensions (fig. 42), which must be capable of being rowed violently by fifteen men? And, of course, it must be done to a fixed price with no escalation.'

Although we did get one or two incredulous brush-offs, we were lucky in finding three yards so intrigued by the idea that they were anxious to tender, and it became a real problem to choose between them. Our choice was, on the surface, just as odd as most other aspects of our enterprise.

A disused chain factory on the banks of an urban canal in Coventry may seem an unlikely place to start building a trireme, but the enthusiasm of the Coventry Boatbuilders' Co-operative and their obvious skill were such that we gave them a contract which, however exciting, can hardly have proved very profitable.

The Co-operative had been established under the leadership of Malcolm Adkins, a lecturer in carpentry at Coventry Polytechnic, in order to build traditional wooden craft to a high standard. They had produced so far only one or two skiffs and a dinghy, and, feeling that they needed assistance in coping with a larger job, had agreed to do the work in co-operation with Marine Training & Development Ltd of Lowestoft. To complicate matters further, therefore, the work had to be started 150 miles away, in a spot as far east as it is possible to go and not at all convenient for poor John Coates. Fortunately from his point of view, at least, the work that was to have been done at Lowestoft took longer than planned, and the trial piece was transferred to Coventry, a much more convenient location.

While John was watching progress on the trial piece, John Morrison and I were attempting to raise funds. An opportunity to do so seemed to present itself in June 1984, when the Posidonia exhibition was due to be held in Piraeus. This event takes place every four years and is the major showplace for the shipping industry. Everyone concerned – owners, builders, insurers, banks, and shipping agencies – mingles, affording an opportunity for us to go around with our begging bowl.

The Hellenic Navy also thought it an appropriate time to announce their offer publicly, and asked me to bring our model of the trireme. This model was an important prop. It had been made to John Coates's original drawings by Norman Gundry, another of John's helpful friends. Norman was also a retired naval constructor, who had worked as an apprentice on HMS *Victory*, and had since made a hobby of model building. His model (fig. 43) was therefore highly professional: although intended only to demonstrate the plans, it also performed perfectly in water. It had but one disadvantage: its size. Knowing that we would need to be able to transport the model easily Norman had also fabricated a casket to accommodate it, felt-lined, with many little devices to hold the delicate structure in place. The whole was about six feet long, and weighed, as I found out when I had to carry it with me to Athens for the exhibition, just under twenty kilos.

That journey was one of the less pleasant episodes in the history of our project. Reasonably enough, Greek customs did not feel inclined to accept my unsubstantiated assurance that what looked so very like a coffin contained a model of an ancient trireme. They insisted on my opening the case. There were twenty-three screws in all. Finding a taxi big enough to hold it was the next problem: while doing so, the carrying straps broke, causing the casket to strike me sharply on the shin at every step. As the taxi had to deposit me some way from the embassy, I was almost incapacitated by the time I reached it. Sir Perry and Lady Rhodes, and their successors Jeremy and Diana Thomas, were unfailingly hospitable to all of us, in spite of what must have been many more pressing considerations.

But, as gradually became apparent, the trireme reconstruction had

Fig. 42 'One-tenth of a ship that last floated 1,500 years ago . . .'

engendered great enthusiasm in Greek Government circles. The Ministry of Culture, headed by the scintillating Melina Mercouris, and the Tourist Board, under her brother Spiros, had appreciated the significance of the project, and were anxious to do whatever they might to help.

I telephoned Anastasias Tzamtzis as soon as I arrived; he was cordial as ever, but sounded a little cagey. A meeting had been arranged at the General Headquarters in the morning. I was to attend (with the wretched case). He felt that it would prove to be 'a significant event'.

And so it turned out. Commodore Kolliniatis, elegantly cool in summer whites, enquired what success we had encountered in raising money? Very little, I had to admit, but we had hopes. 'Then,' he said, very straight-faced 'this document may be useful,' and he presented me with a short official letter saying that the Hellenic Navy and the Greek Government would undertake to pay the full cost of the reconstruction. The Trust was to be

Fig. 43 The founders of the Trireme Trust, (left to right) John Coates, Professor John Morrison and Frank Welsh, with Norman Gundry's model of the trireme

responsible for completing the design, providing the trial piece, specification and working drawings, and advising on construction. On completion the trireme would be commissioned into the Greek Navy, but the Trust would have access to the completed ship for research and trials. Only when I had finished reading the letter did the Commodore let himself smile, and show how pleased he was to be able to give me this splendid news.

We were, of course, gratefully ready, once over the first shock, to accept this remarkably generous offer, which meant that from being the hobby-horse of a group of elderly gentlemen, the rebuilding of the Salamis trireme had become an officially established project. There was, however, one proviso. Due to the exigencies of the budget a strict schedule was necessary, which demanded that tenders should be invited by the end of August 1984 – only a couple of months away. This necessitated speedy action; John Coates and John Morrison went immediately to Athens in order to clarify details, and to sign the agreement which became known as the Athens Concordat. John Coates had then exactly four weeks to finalize drawings and write the specification, if the programme was to be met. This would have been impossible without Dorian Dymoke's help. He willingly turned his hand to the complexities of moulding and sidings, scarfs and butts, fairing and faying, tenons and dowels, and all the ancient jargon of shipbuilding in wood.

Exactly four weeks later John presented himself back in Athens with tracings, prints and copies of the specification, still in manuscript since there had been no time for typing. These had immediately to be translated into Greek by Commodore Kolliniatis and Commander Platis, the officer who as to be in charge of the project. John had to try to explain the precise nature of such things as futtocks, treenails, nibends and clenching, terms not to be found in any English/Greek dictionary. But professional was speaking to professional, and there was a complete meeting of minds which left John convinced that the trireme was in the best of hands.

He had to return to the trial piece, which after a slow start was progressing remarkably well, owing to the skill and adaptability of the two craftsmen working on it at Coventry. Richard Eberhart and Ian Oliver are both young men, typical of a new sort of craftsman, who have chosen a trade that appeals to them and mastered it as well as any of their predecessors. Their intelligent innovative approach made the job go swimmingly.

The trial piece, it may be remembered, was not only to serve as a sample of the construction, but as a proving ground for the oar system which would be more stringent than that of the mock-up. At Earls Court we had seen that with only four oars being pulled at anything approaching full power the water in the tank would very quickly slop over. The trial piece with fifteen oars would be tested in the Thames, when without this risk we could really see how the system worked at full stretch.

The occasion for doing this was eminently suitable: the Henley Royal

Regatta of 1985. We had been invited to introduce our trial piece there and given an excellent mooring just in front of the Leander Club. Unlike our Greenwich conference, when there had been no time for any preliminary testing, we did have an opportunity to see how the trial piece behaved before taking it to Henley. John had found a convenient and secluded spot in an ornamental Victorian moat in the grounds of Coombe Abbey, near Coventry. It proved just as well that we had privacy for our first attempt at the tricky job of persuading a one-sided, inherently unstable object to float, and continue to float under the stresses of hard rowing. Part of the experiment was to test a theory that the edge-jointed planks would form so tight a seam that no caulking would be needed, and the trial piece had therefore been left untreated. It took very little time to disprove that particular theory, since once in the moat our trial piece started to settle gently to the bottom. John and his assistants had to caulk it as best they could under water, before pumping it dry.

Eventually all was put right and the buoyancy drums were rigged so that the waterline would be at the right level when fifteen oarsmen were on board. The honour of being the first crew for 1,500 years to test even part of a trireme fell to the Warwick University Boat Club. John reported on their arrival as follows:

> The first crew to try out the trial section came from the Warwick University Boat Club and I was glad to see some girls amongst them. With doubting anticipation and disbelief written all over their faces, they climbed over the moat wall and so aboard. After much general badinage (some naturally aimed at me) all oars were manned and foot stretchers adjusted. First we just tested the stroke to show the range of postures to people brought up to sliding seats and nearly horizontal oar handles, then off we went, fairly chaotically at first as the closely packed oars hit each other, but after several more starts and about ten minutes the whole thing came together. Now everywhere was amazement and pleasure! The stroke rate was quickened and shortened a little: striking rate rose to over thirty strokes a minute. Here after five years' design and development was the first intimation of the trireme in action. That crew volunteered en bloc to pull the ship in Greece and departed enthusiastic and two inches taller.

The need for adjustments had immediately become apparent to me. Some oarports needed easing open a little wider, and oar loops needed another twist as they stretched. Otherwise we were ready for a heavier and more experienced crew from Worcester to try their hand at pulling an archaic ship. Led by their president, Don Cox, the Worcester Rowing Club team of rowing veterans settled in with a more robust style of comment and backchat. This was clearly a team best left to work it out themselves, which I felt they obviously wanted to do. Stroked by their president, one file at a time worked their oars until they had got a consistent stroke. They then all pulled together and quickly their performance became a most impressive exhibition, as stroke raised the rate of striking. 'Up a notch,' he would cry and they all kept together beautifully. The trial section became alive, fascinating all bystanders. Up the rate went until it was over forty to the minute. Real power was sending water down the moat at a rate that could never have been seen there before! The crew was hooked by the surprise and excitement of their achievement, and they also volunteered to help to crew the trireme in Greece. They had been a thrilling sight, giving a really firm and confident intimation of the trireme at full power. This ship is going to surprise, amaze and excite a lot of people, I thought. There could be no doubt now that the project is worthwhile! Certainly the trial section worked and was fit to be exposed to the critical eyes of rowing men at the Henley Royal Regatta.

Although the Coombe Abbey trials had been successful, the move to Henley aroused some trepidation. The police had to be notified and permission obtained to transport the trial piece by road, for unlike the mock-up, it did not slot into a horse-box. We were moving into a larger and more complex set of problems. At Coombe the section had been quietly moored in a stagnant moat, while at Henley we would be on a public towpath in a river feeling the effects of the wettest June in decades. Even the short river trip between Hobbs' boatyard, where it would be launched, and the Leander Club mooring was fraught with unpleasing possibilities.

An added complication came when the dotty sub-culture of the animal-liberationist-anarchist-revolutionary-smash-everything-dirty-shirt variety enthusiastically took up the challenge posed by Henley, and announced their intention of breaking up the regatta. Many, including the *Daily Telegraph* and the Thames Valley police, took their threats seriously enough, but we adopted a more relaxed attitude: after all, if one were going to attempt physical violence at a sporting event one would be ill advised to choose

Fig. 44 *The trial piece being rowed at Henley*

one at which the participants were composed entirely of muscular young men armed with large oars and with a convenient river to hand!

As it turned out Henley was a great success, without interruptions of any sort. Hundreds of the world's best oarsmen came to try their hands at rowing a portion of a trireme, and the trial piece stood up nobly to the strain (fig. 44). Even the weather was kind.

One fact that particularly struck the visiting oarsmen was that the underwater area of the trireme was so small, about 100 square metres, which amounts to some 0.6 m per man. A modern racing eight, the fastest oared

136

boat in existence, has twice that – 1.2 square metres per man. In other words, a modern oarsman has twice as much water resistance to overcome as one rowing in a trireme had. Our trireme would skim over the surface, as was evident from her hull section. Even at the fullest midships section very little of the hull would be below the waterline; there would be even less forward, and nothing at all aft.

The Trust received much publicity which we now, in a rather blasé fashion, accepted as our due, and we started to enrol volunteers for the first full crew to row in the sea trials of the completed ship. There were, however, still heretics about unconvinced by what we now, with surely some justification, considered a well-tested design. Richard Burnell wrote in a letter to *Rowing Magazine*:

Dear Sir,

If the experts say that the trireme had three banks of oars with one oarsman per oar, so be it. But if the model displayed at Henley this year, and described in the August issue of *Rowing Magazine*, works – it will be a miracle.

Firstly, with all oars the same length but working at different angles on each deck, the path of the bottom bank of blades through the water will approximate to the path of blades in a tub pair, the path of the middle bank blade will be similar to that of the blades in a high-sided sea whaler, and the top bank blades will operate more like the blades of a paddlewheel. Whilst the bottom blades work parallel to the surface of the water, the top blades will 'scoop' the water, first pressing down on the surface (tending to lift the boat out of the water) and then upwards (tending to bury the boat).

The length of arc described by the blades in the water will vary for each bank shortest for the top and longest for the bottom bank. The resistance of the water will also vary through the stroke, the bottom blades being fully covered (though shallow) throughout the stroke, whilst at the opposite extreme the top bank blades will be fully covered only briefly in mid-stroke. Yet every single blade must enter and leave the water in perfect unison if eighty-five blades on each side of the boat are to be correctly synchronized.

But that is only the tip of the iceberg. The 'scooping' action of the upper banks of oars will induce a 'bouncing' motion (as in a Canadian canoe), which will lead to longitudinal oscillation (pitching). On a waterline of say 90′, with a fifty-tonne displacement boat travelling at 5–10 m.p.h., that pitching will be very considerable. Additionally the formidable top hamper illustrated in the model, above a relatively slim waterline profile, will certainly encourage rolling.

The height of rowlock above water level for the lowest bank of oars looks to be quite inadequate to cope with a rolling and pitching boat, even if the water were calm. But it will not be calm, even in still water on a calm day, because the movement of the boat itself will generate a wave motion, and with such a long boat, and such short oars, the oarsmen will surely be trying to row in their own self-generated waves. With a number of such Leviathans operating together, turning, stopping and accelerating as they seek a ramming position, the water would soon be churned up to the point where the bottom bank of oars could not operate at all.

I admire the enterprise and hope it can be made to work. But I'm glad I shall not be one of the 150 oarsmen when it first puts to sea.

John Coates rather indignantly replied:

Mr Burnell, in his letter in your October issue, accepts that the trireme had three banks of oars of equal length, but seems to doubt if the arrangement of those banks demonstrated at Henley last July actually works. Maybe he did not then have an opportunity to see for himself by trying it out, as a large number of our visitors to the trial section did.

The demonstrated fact is that it does work. Several crews at Henley and elsewhere achieved a stroke of about forty to the minute in good time and with real power – an exhilarating sight. Mr Burnell's 'scooping', bouncing and pitching simply do not occur. The thole-pins of the lowest banks of oars are as high above the water as the rowlocks of a naval cutter. The trireme is much too long to generate a wave motion (which is indeed why it is such a long ship!) and, contrary to Mr Burnell's belief, the length of arc described by the blades in the water is exactly the same in each bank, as a little geometrical consideration will show.

Many of our visitors at Henley, seeing the slope of the top oars, asked, 'How could those possibly work?' We said, 'Try them and see,' and without exception they found that the slope was quite easy to manage.

We are nowadays just unused to sloping oars; once they were common in sea-going and heavy harbour craft. All our oarmen visitors at Henley who actually tried the oars appeared to be quite convinced of the practicability of what they saw. About 200 were convinced enough to volunteer to crew the trireme in Greek waters.

It will be by no miracle, as Mr Burnell suggests, that the trireme will work but by the fruit of many years of painstaking historical research, underwater archaeology and technical design.

Other visitors did not share Mr Burnell's doubt. Herman Petrusky, a well-known German oarsman, wrote enthusiastically in *Das Logbuch*, July 1985:

It became obvious that the English have a knack in their dealings with the world of learning. While a popular presentation of scientific knowledge in Germany quickly gets the reputation of 'pseudo-science' and is therefore largely avoided, the English do not hesitate to present such work during a popular event in a popular way. Besides the photographs, drawings and reconstruction plans for triremes which were on show, T-shirts with emblems, badges, brooches, trireme picture-books for children as well as learned books were also on sale. The trial section itself represents scientific knowledge which can be touched. Everyone, from grandma to toddler, was free to clamber about the wooden structure of the trireme, to sit on the seats and to move the oars or to fall between the numerous beams right down into the bilge. Here in Germany one may be sure that the building control department would prohibit entry to it. Those who wanted to do more than just clamber about, move oars 4.5 m long, and to know everything that was known about triremes could satisfy themselves too. . . .

Then there it was – I climbed in – had no difficulties in orientating myself – yes, here were the thranites, a little below were the zygians, and right down there were the thalamians – not so low or so much in the dark as imagined even though the trial section was fitted overhead with a complete deck to guard it against the weather – this is not the case in the original ship. Then I move the oars: they work, and work more easily than imagined – I am pulling a trireme!

Only one modification was needed as a result of the thorough pounding that the trial piece experienced at Henley, and that was simple enough, although highly significant. Originally we had placed the oars aft of the thole-pins, i.e. on the side further from the rower. Some objections had been made to this, as a result of which we reversed them, hanging the oar forward of the thole-pins. It was discovered that this was not satisfactory, since if any one of the 170 oars stuck in the water for any reason until it met the after-edge of the oarport, it would jam at the end of the stroke causing chaos. Hanging the oar *aft* obviated this possibility, for oars can only jam at the beginning of a stroke, as the oar is forced free by its passage through the water. Incidentally, as this is still the universal practice among small boats in the Aegean, perhaps, given hindsight, it ought to have been obvious.

Meanwhile, back in Greece, the Navy had been pushing ahead with evaluating the tenders they had received. The process had not proved easy for there were very few yards capable of offering a convincing tender, and it was not until May 1985, ten months after the specification was completed, that the contract was placed with the Tsakakos yard of Keratsini, near Piraeus. The two Tsakakos brothers, Dimitrios and Nikolaous, were able to inspect the trial piece closely before it went into the water at Henley.

They were able to see exactly how all the joints were being made, with tenons firmly set in the closely spaced mortices, and the difficult classic scarf that had to be used on the keel. For the first time the trireme could be imagined as a real thing; we had built one tenth of the ship, without encountering any insurmountable difficulties. In doing so, a Coventry boatyard, newly established, had managed to acquire woodworking skills that had long since disappeared. We felt hopeful that the Greek builders would do equally well.

CHAPTER

7

The building

IMMEDIATELY after Henley, George Dracopoulos arranged to take the trial piece on one of his Empros Line ships out to the Tsakakos yard, where it would serve as a guide to the shipwrights. Before it arrived, however, the Tsakakos brothers had some of their most essential work to do, the procurement of the timbers. This was not an easy task. Even for the much smaller *Argo*, Tim Severin had been able to track down only a single stand of timber that suited his purposes. John Coates had been equally specific about the lengths and qualities of the wood he required, and, since John is not satisfied with anything much short of perfection, all the construction materials were subjected to a searching examination.

When he came to inspect the timber that Tsakakos had found for the keel, John pronounced both the appearance of the iroko and the Oregon pine planking exactly right, wonderfully close and regularly grained, and of good quality. He had, however a bad shock on measuring the moisture content of the Oregon pine. All his calculations of hull-design had been based on timber whose moisture content averaged 12 per cent, which gave a specific gravity of 0.56. A higher moisture content inevitably meant a higher specific gravity, and therefore more weight, the consequences of which, for a ship as precisely designed as the trireme, would have included a complete recalculation of the heights of oarsmen's seats, ports, tholes – in fact the whole internal construction. And the timber samples were very wet; they showed a specific gravity of 0.643, which meant wood that was nearly 15 per cent heavier than calculated, and a ship two and a half tons heavier, riding too low in the water to allow the thalamians to operate properly.

Fig. 45 Greek ceremony of blessing includes a cross nailed to the prow

It was, however, possible that the pieces John had selected were unusually wet, and that the timber would dry out further before it came to be used. To check this, John put the samples in the cool oven of his wife's Aga, and after a few hours it had dried to precisely the desired level. This use of advanced technology allayed John's fears: the most important materials had passed their tests.

The contract with Tsakakos had been signed on 2 May 1985. As befitted so careful a specification, it was an agreement that might equally have covered the construction of a modern frigate, drawn up with exemplary exactitude; among its many clauses was one stipulating that a new, specially designed and secure shed should be provided for the building. This was a practical necessity, for the Tsakakos enterprise otherwise consists of a patch of ground where fishing-boats are built in the open air, adjoining the main highway between Piraeus and Corinth, and convenient for Keratsini harbour. Although lying under the very heights where Xerxes' throne was placed, it is not a romantic area. The quayside is decaying and despondent; cats and rats live in unamicable juxtaposition; sea-girt Salamis is seen through a fleet of laid-up shipping; the temple of Eleusis, once home to the most sacred rites, is neighbour to an immense cement factory. The throne from which the Great King observed the battle would now overlook docks and a power station. Our earlier dreams of building the trireme on the sandy beach of a secluded island clashed similarly with the depressing reality of Keratsini.

But there were sound practical reasons for choosing a location so close to Athens and Piraeus, where sub-contractors for spars, metalwork and fittings would readily be found, and where naval supervision could easily be exercised. The enterprise got off to a good start. The picturesque ceremony of blessing was carried out by four priests, and a cross was nailed to the timbers of the prow (fig. 45). John Coates and I paid visits in December and November 1985 and were able to report that progress was very good. There had been, it is true, some delay in the shipment of live oak from Georgia for the vital tenons, but Tsakakos, as well as completing the shed, had laid out the lines of the ship clearly and accurately. This operation is one requiring considerable skill and care: the plans are reproduced at the true scale — ten times larger than in the drawing — on a prepared floor, and serve then as guides for shaping the timbers. Unless it is properly done, subsequent errors are inevitable, but Tsakakos, assisted by a naval architect, had managed it quickly and well. John recorded at the time, 'The whole visit was most encouraging; I had seen all the signs of a good job to come, and the close interest and professional advice of the Hellenic Navy overseers gave me added assurance that this tricky building operation was going to be successful.'

By the time Captain Tzamtsis and I paid our first visit to the yard good progress had also been made with the construction itself. Sheltered by the new shed, the keel of the ship had been laid on a steel frame designed to support her during construction, and to avoid deflection as the weight of the hull grew. The keel itself, with its complex scarfs, was complete. The scimitar-like stem and stern posts, all carved from good timbers of hard iroko, were in place. Wooden moulds, which traced the sections of the ship as the hull progressively widened from either end, had been made from the laid-off lines: these would act as a guide to the workers as they bent

Fig. 46 Work on the trireme in the Tsakakos ship shed

the planks into shape. Ancient shipwrights may have done this by eye –
or with a few key moulds only, as indeed modern Greek boat-builders do
– but it would have been unrealistic to attempt to do so on a project of
this size when we were resurrecting skills that had not been employed for
a millennium and a half. The moulds were held in place by longitudinal
battens running the full length of the ship at different levels. Taken together
with the keel, stem and stern, the whole outline of the ship was thus traced
in timber. A higher section of the shed had been built to accommodate the
huge rounded stern, which curved up some thirty feet from the floor.
Although I had been telling everyone for some months that our ship was
big, I was quite unprepared for her sheer size as she rose in the shed with
her final shape already visible (fig. 46).

The Hellenic Navy was on site in the immaculately turned-out person
of Lieutenant Christos Lelentzis, who had been appointed naval overseer
for the ship. He had a section of Tsakakos's office, with a spotlessly tidy
desk on which the only visible paper was a large building programme showing every stage of the contract progressing towards a completion date of
August 1986. In spite of two months' delay in delivery of the live oak, Commander Stavros Platis, who was in overall charge of the project, considered

that the trireme should be ready for commissioning at least by September, since 'things are going to go much faster in the future'.

Only three shipwrights – Nikos Tsakakos, Alexis Kapsalis and Michael Kozonis, all impressively skilled in the use of traditional tools – were employed at that stage, but when planking-up started in the New Year, another three to six were to be added. The work would then become largely repetitive and might be expected to advance rapidly. It had certainly done so during the building of the trial piece in Coventry, although they had not found the initial stages easy and had taken longer than they had expected with the work of laying off, making the keel, and carving the planks nearest to it out of solid wood as the sharp angle of the hull there demanded. Much of this more complex work had already been satisfactorily completed in Keratsini, and there was no reason to expect that the remainder of this job would not be comparatively straightforward.

While Tsakakos's building contract covered much the most important part of the construction, a certain amount of work would remain to be done after he had finished. He would remedy any defects that might be found in testing, but his responsibility would then be taken over by the Hellenic Navy, which would complete the rigging, fitting out, and stability and swamp tests. When these were done, sea trials would start. It was at that point that the Trireme Trust hoped to be able to play a part by providing the crew of oarsmen that would be trained to operate the ship. Then we would prove, once and for all, whether John Morrison's theories and John Coates's design worked when put to the ultimate test of the open sea.

By February 1986 the difficult planks next to the keel had been carved, laid in place, and jointed together. Commander Platis believed that the project would now start to move more quickly, and Tsakakos was confident that the ship would be ready for the water in August as planned. But the work failed to gather momentum. Stavros Platis was kept extremely busy by much more pressing naval business; the extra workmen failed to appear; Lieutenant Lelentzis's progress chart fell further behind. Matters were not improved when, on a visit in April 1986, John Coates found a serious defect which could have had quite grave consequences. Possibly in an endeavour to speed up work, the oak tenons in the lower planks had been fitted quite loosely instead of being hammered tight into their mortices. This might not have mattered too much if the looseness had been across the width of the plank, but it was endways on. Instead of tightly connecting the ship along its whole length, the most important planks were now worryingly flexible.

Longitudinal bending strength had always been the most critical point of John's design, and that strength could now be seriously impaired.

The only really satisfactory solution would have been to have scrapped the defective work and to have started again; such a decision would, however, have proved intolerably expensive and time-consuming and might well have wrecked the whole project, so a second method was adopted, and the defective joints were all sealed with a water-resistant glue. This would at least restore something of the rigidity that was missing, but the joints remained a worrying and basic weakness.

In May John Morrison and I attended a ceremony at which Melina Mercouris, the famous actress and Greek Minister of Culture, introduced the trireme to the Greek public. The Mercouris, Melina and her brother Spiros, had taken a lively interest in the trireme from the beginning and had joined with the Hellenic Navy in promoting it. When we visited the ship it seemed to us that John Coates's strictures had been taken to heart, and that the yard had undertaken all the corrective measures he required. To our inexperienced eyes, however, it did not seem possible that the work, which had not advanced much since February, could possibly be anywhere near completion. With a view to eventual sea trials, we paid another visit to Poros where we were able, as the guests of Lieutenant Commander Rouskas, to take a closer look at the Naval School. It would be hard to find a pleasanter place than the Hellenic Navy Petty Officer School at Poros. Occupying a small peninsula near the junction of Poros town with the main island, the headquarters building was constructed in 1846 as the summer palace of King Otto and Queen Amalia. Light grey and elegant, with palm trees and formal gardens on one side and an open view to the mountains of Troizen on the other, it must be one of the most attractive modern buildings in Greece.

The school itself was founded earlier, in 1827, one of the first institutions in independent Greece. In that year Admiral Edward Codrington took the British fleet from Poros to Navarino, where, in command of the British, French and Russian squadrons, he fought the decisive battle which secured Greek independence. That remarkable character Captain Frank Hastings was the school's first commander, and is buried in the grounds. Hastings was by far the most effective of that odd bunch of European philhellenes who turned up to give them a hand against the Turks. A man of means and a fine sailor, he made what the Hellenic Maritime Museum describes as an 'enormous contribution' to the cause of Greek liberation. In 1825 Hastings supervised the building in England of the steam warship the *Karteria*, and contributed to the expenses of her construction. Less than 300 tons, the *Karteria* was nevertheless a powerful ship: she had twin 85 hp engines, was capable of 7 knots under steam, and carried an armament of eight 68-pounders, the most formidable piece of the period and capable of throwing red-hot shot. Under Hastings she became the first steam warship to see action, and destroyed a Turkish fleet in the bay of Solona. Hastings was mortally wounded in action, and died in 1828.

Commander Rouskas, an instructor at the School, was living in a charming house on an islet connected to the School by a steep bridge, which gave at least the illusion of an independent solitude. Sitting in his gardens watching the sunset over the mountains, we were convinced that Poros was by far the best place for our trireme trials. However it might be blowing outside, the waters in the Poros straits would be protected; and if the Navy would agree to our using the School to house the trial crew, many other dangers would be avoided. It is never easy to organize even an eights crew, as Oxford discovered before the 1987 boat race, and having some 200 young people scattered about in tavernas, hotels and private rooms would be something of a nightmare. A nice safe barracks which would foster at least the semblance of discipline was much to be preferred.

Agreeing that, in the interests of any future crew, we should explore the facilities of the island (and since we were travelling on cheap air tickets that insisted upon our spending at least seven days in Greece), we hired a pair of decrepit bicycles. John on a sit-up-and-beg bicycle, with panama hat, linen jacket, rolled-up trousers, and sandals, was instantly recognizable as an English don or perhaps a colonial Bishop; even divested of these props he was unmistakable. While attempting to undress modestly in the vicinity of some unclad females, we recalled that episode in John Evelyn's diary, where Evelyn, caught short and compelled to quit his coach in Charing Cross, ordered his servant to cover his face, since 'they are not likely to know mine arse again'.

But in view of the lack of progress at the shipyard, sea trials that year were beginning to look ever less likely, and our apprehensions were justified in August when Tsakakos asked for an extension until January 1987.

In retrospect it is now clear that in attempting to operate the project as though it were a conventional naval building programme, we had asked too much of Tsakakos. His enterprise was not adapted to following complex plans, to working within fine tolerances and to an ambitious deadline. Even

Fig. 47 The interior – view from for'ard, starboard side

though he had given them full drawings and a comprehensive specification, John Coates wryly observed that these were treated more as holy relics to be preserved in the office than as actual working documents. Tsakakos constantly asked for answers which could easily have been provided by a quick reference to the drawings, and much needless anxiety and delay was thereby generated. And, of course, all the while the trial piece itself was lying unregarded in a corner of the shed, a tangible indication of exactly how every detail was executed.

There is some truth in the old saying that an engineer builds to the nearest thousandth of an inch, a carpenter to the nearest eighth of an inch, and the shipwright to the nearest ship; also that Noah was the last boat-builder to complete on time, and then only because he would have drowned

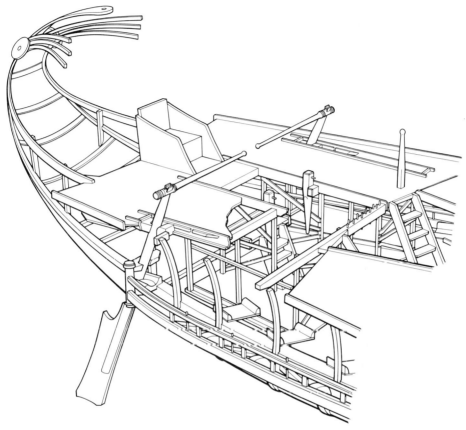

Fig. 48 Detailed drawing of the stern

if he had not. Nothing short of John Coates being present the whole time could have avoided the errors and delays, and that is what finally had to happen.

Between September 1986 and July 1987 John spent twenty weeks in Greece, overseeing every detail of the job, advising on problems, and liaising with the Navy. With his help Tsakakos finished the ship, and did so in great style. The difficulties, which we ought perhaps to have foreseen, were inevitable; but the achievement of Demetrios Tsakakos and his team in building this highly sophisticated craft, rediscovering ancient techniques as they went along, must be one of the most remarkable in modern boat-building.

The construction of the high stern is an example of the complex tasks faced by the builders. One of the most striking characteristics of all ancient galleys, it is shown in representations of all types from Mycenean to Roman times. Taken in conjunction with the remaining timbers of the Marsala Punic ship, the general shape of the trireme's stern was well understood.

Translating the design into reality was, however, no easy matter. Such dramatic three-dimensional curves are unknown in modern vessels, and no wooden-boat builder, or indeed any other craftsman, has any experience of shaping timber in this fashion. In order to help Tsakakos with this, James Paffet, a retired naval constructor and vice-president of the Royal Institution of Naval Architects, made a model of the stern, ensuring that the planks could in fact be bent into the graceful curves the design demanded. John himself made a full-scale mould for the builders to follow (fig. 49). But it was Tsakakos and his men who succeeded in creating this beautiful piece of craftsmanship. Viewed from the stern, the sickle curve of the hull gives an impression of lightness and urgency. One can see exactly how it caught the imagination of so many artists; it is itself a piece of abstract sculpture in wood.

For the first three weeks of his protracted stay in Greece John Coates was the guest of Demetrios Tsakakos in his flat in Piraeus and in his country home in the Peloponnese, where they would retreat at weekends to view the progress of another Tsakakos project — the new marble-clad parish church, which seemed to be making rather better progress than was the trireme.

In most ways the two men are entirely opposite. Where John is tall, thin, self-contained and reserved, Demetrios is short, portly and effervescently demonstrative; John is studious and fastidious, Tsakakos is a man who enjoys the pleasures of the table and a crowded family life. Nor was communication between them easy; to start with John spoke little Greek, and Demetrios had only a few words of English. The one's loud and rapid Greek was as difficult for the other to follow as the other's precise and qualified English. But in spite of these dissimilarities they had two things in common — a total dedication to the work in hand, and an unflagging energy, especially in finding solutions to difficult problems. Their methods naturally differed; John settled down with a fountain pen and a pad of paper while Demetrios argued, persuaded and cajoled. Both, however, deployed wide practical knowledge, and the finished vessel is a memorial to their collaboration, recorded in more than one builder's plaque fixed to

Fig. 49 The curving timbers of the upswept stern

different parts of the ship prominently displaying the name of JHON COATES!

I saw something of their co-operation during a visit in September '86. Tsakakos wanted a progress report from John which he could submit to the Navy. John explained that he had no contractual standing in the matter, being merely an adviser. There was an interpreter, but he was hardly necessary: Demetrios can make himself understood. For five minutes he bounced about the room, picking up completed samples – cushions, stretchers, tholepins – gesticulating towards the shed, and pouring out a torrent of finest Greek. John sat composedly behind a desk, and expressed himself in two sentences. After three or four rounds of this strange dialogue a satisfactory compromise was reached, and the work carried on.

But even John's devoted support could not spark enough energy in the yard to keep the work on schedule. There were still only two men employed at a time when John calculated that forty man-months of work remained to be done. Those men were depressed by the appalling amount of work that faced them, but Tsakakos claimed thet Greek labour laws made it impossibly expensive to take on men who would have to be laid off a few months later. It was once again painfully clear that even the delayed January 1987 date could not be achieved. The possibility – an expensive one – of importing some of the Coventry work-force was seriously canvassed. We were extremely worried that when the extended contract-completion date still found the ship unfinished, the whole project would grind to a halt. Captain Tzamtzis was comforting. He explained that things were ordered differently in Greece; somehow, and he did not know exactly how, all would come right, and the ship would be finished; we should not concern outselves unduly, but have faith.

By way of a brief respite from trireme problems, my wife and I persuaded John to take a couple of days off to look at some sites associated with the history of the trireme. We had hoped to visit Poros, which John had not yet had the opportunity of considering as a location for the trials, but sea passages were too rough even for modern ferries and we decided to take a look at Artemisium instead, the scene of the first naval engagement of the campaign that ended in the Battle of Salamis.

The island of Evvia (ancient Euboea), lying parallel to the east coast of Attica, is one of the largest in Greece, more than 120 miles from north to south. In spite of its proximity to Athens, Evvia has many unspoilt beaches and beautiful rugged scenery, yet it is almost unknown to foreign tourists. At Chalkis (ancient Aulis) the island is only a hundred yards from the mainland: it was here that the Greek fleets gathered before the siege of Troy, and here Iphigenia was sacrificed by her father Agamemnon to ensure fair winds. Unlike the other coasts of Attica, it is possible here to recapture the classical world most strikingly, aided by the comparative absence of visitors. The Amphitraeon, in a wooded valley on the mainland a few miles from Chalkis, is one of the finest sites in Greece, a miniature Epidauros, quiet and secluded, where one may wander unnoticed and undisturbed.

The original Persian invasion fleet of 1207 triremes which Xerxes, according to Herodotus, mustered for the Salamis campaign had been reduced by huge losses in a summer storm off the coast of Magnesia, but there were still 800 or 900 ships left to support the army advancing towards Thermopylae – much more than a match for the 271 vessels that the Athenians and their allies could muster. When the Greeks saw how gravely they were outnumbered, there was, as always, an animated discussion, in which a vociferous body of opinion argued in favour of retreat through the channel that separates Evvia from the mainland (fig. 1).

While the argument was going on the Persians detached 200 ships to round the island and take the Greeks in the rear, the same tactic that they later tried at Salamis. Realizing what had happened, and detecting the opportunity offered by the enemy of splitting his forces, Themistocles persuaded the Greek fleet to offer battle, although they were still outnumbered more than two to one. By skilful tactics, which included delaying action until late in the day, thus restricting the Persians' ability to take advantage of the numerical superiority that, given time, must inevitably have told, the Greeks won the first day's battle after a damaging fight, and drew on the second. The 200 ships of the detached Persian force had all, meanwhile, been wrecked off the coast of Evvia, demonstrating for the second time within a few days the vulnerability of triremes to unsettled weather.

Between the battle and the storms, the Persian force had thus been further reduced by some 300 ships, which must have entailed a loss of 60,000 men. Without this drastic weakening the subsequent Greek victory at Salamis would have been impossible. We therefore made a pilgrimage to the wild coast of Artemisium, and to the beach where the triremes had been drawn out, awaiting the signal for battle. The beach lies in a great curve of shingle, looking out towards the hills above Thermopylae, and forms a much more romantic view than does that from Piraeus across to Salamis today.

When John returned from this short holiday to live *en famille* with the Tzakakoses, sleeping on a sofa in the living-room and rather over-exposed to Greek television at full blast, which acted as a backdrop to family discussions, he must still have looked in need of another change. This was effected and his existence made much more agreeable when our Ambassador in Athens, Sir Jeremy Thomas, visiting the yard, offered him quarters in the Embassy. As well as permitting him to work quietly, the move enabled John to keep in touch with a new-found and most valuable ally.

Captain Colin McGregor, RN, Naval and Air Attaché to the British Embassy in Athens, is everyone's ideal dashing sailor. Blue-eyed and hand-some (he would make a better James Bond than any of the actors that have tried their hand) he worked, discreetly and behind the scenes, what must be accounted miracles. It needed all these, together with John Coates's patient attention, to push the project towards completion. And in late September an improvement was discernible: Commander Platis found him-self able to devote more time to advancing the work, and a livelier tempo developed.

In John Coates's intervals at home he pursued experiments on the still unresolved design of the hypozoma. Everything about this element of design was hypothetical – the position in (or around) the hull, the composition of the rope, the methods of securing and of twisting, and the degree of tight-ness. A wooden hull is a wooden hull, even if constructed according to archaic practices, but the hypozoma was a factor beyond anyone's experience.

And it proved every bit as difficult to put into practice as we feared. Dorian Dymoke had produced his model of the tensioning gear, but the behaviour of the rope under load, John discovered, was complex. He wrote at the time:

> During the autumn 1985 I had started to investigate the behaviour of natural fibre rope when tightened by twisting as in a tourniquet. This was to find out how the 40 mm diameter ropes of the hypozomata would behave in the ship. Ever since the introduction of iron bars, steel ropes and bottle screws, twisted rope has been little used to exert tensions in construction, and there seemed to be no data about it available today. What force could be sustained by the four ropes stretched from one

end of the ship to the other? What torque would be called for? By how many turns would it have to be wound up? How should the ends be secured? I could find no one in the rope business who any longer knew. Some crude experiments in my workshop showed how much rope relaxed after being twisted and held between two fixed points and at a certain number of turns. It looked as though only about one third of the breaking tension of the rope could be sustained for a long time in a tourniquet. Better experiments were needed, and Dorian Dymoke and Norman Grundy devised a testing apparatus and Norman Grundy made it for me. A long series of experiments followed. One had to allow periods of time to elapse between readings so I returned to the rig from the drawing-board for another reading over a period of some months. It was now obvious that all this should have been done earlier in the development of the trireme reconstruction. I am afraid I had just overlooked the actual complexities of what seemed such a simple affair. It is easy to be tripped up by the subtleties of the apparently crude devices of the past.

John sought advice from ropemakers at Bridport, the centre of traditional ropemaking (exemplified in the cant expression for a hangman's noose – a Bridport dagger), but as the months went by the hypozoma still refused to disclose its secrets. Even finding natural rope of the correct size presented problems – and was the rope itself to be hemp, flax, sisal, manilla or agave?

For his part John Morrison was engaged in seeing the book *The Athenian Trireme* through the press. This incisive work reviewed all the information John had collected over the previous fifty years, and described the principles on which John Coates's designs had been made. It was generally received with the enthusiasm it warranted, with one singular exception. In a review in the *Mariner's Mirror*, that repository of trireme lore, Dr Lucien Basch once more painstakingly went back to Tarn and rehearsed all the old arguments. He concluded his review thus:

> In view of such objections which go to the very foundations of the whole project, those which concern the details of its execution might seem futile. However, one might ask oneself what is the fidelity of a reconstruction which sets out to be as faithful as possible, where the thickness of the tenons, to give but one example, is fixed at 12 mm not upon the basis of any archaeological evidence which is totally lack-

ing, but simply because the thickness of the tenons of the Marsala ship (9 mm) was judged after testing to be inadequate. One might on the same grounds, question the use of polysulphide sealant in order to secure the watertightness of the hull, if only because this process will betray our ignorance of one essential aspect of the hull of the trireme, its caulking. It is true that this question is described as being both important and 'humdrum'. That said, why will the trieris of the eighties not work perfectly? As M. Willicombe so truly said during the preliminary discussion at Greenwich, 'oarsmen geometry is dictated by the vital statistics of the oarsmen and not by hydrodynamics'. These are strong and wise words. Thanks to vital statistics which will soon be put to use, to the talents and calculations of J. F. Coates, the architect of the plans, and to technical progress (such as polysulphide sealant), I am convinced that the 'trieris of the eighties' will prove herself far better on the sea than did the unfortunate Imperial Trireme of Napoleon III. Even so, it would be erroneous to believe that this ship with three banks of oarsmen, which will prove to be of the greatest interest from the point of view of the sport of rowing, will be a reproduction of one of those triremes which were the glory of Athens at the victory of Salamis from 480 till the defeat of Amorgos in 322.

And like Tarn before him, Dr Basch dismissed one of the more important bits of evidence in a footnote. 'In this paper I have not felt it necessary to discuss the so called Talos vase which is in the Ruvo collection at Jatta, analysed in depth by J. S. Morrison in *Greek Oared Ships*, because the whole of this analysis rests in fact upon a parallel with the Lenormant Relief.'

In a temperate reply Morrison and Coates went immediately to the nub of the argument:

> M. Basch has misunderstood. The arrangement of the oars proposed in 1941 and 1968 was diagrammatic, set out with the sole intention of demonstrating the theory that oars at three levels in a galley could, rather surprisingly, be of the same length, as the ancient evidence required. The step now taken in *The Athenian Trireme* is for a naval architect to fit this system of oars into a properly designed hull taking into account the rough maxima of length and breadth provided by the excavation of the Zea shipsheds which were certainly built to accommodate triremes. There is no abandonment of anything or radical

reshaping, but there is the crucial application of the laws of physics and the techniques of wooden-boat building to the previously proposed theory which has stood the test of time.

Dr Basch seemed not to have understood that what we were trying to do was to create a ship which would be able to perform in the same way that we knew ancient triremes had. The laws of hydrodynamics, mechanics and physics have not changed since the fifth century BC (although the vital statistics of oarsmen might to some extent have done so). If our ship was able to match the recorded performances (a big 'if'), and conformed to the available evidence, it would indeed be a fair 'reproduction of one of those triremes which were the glory of Athens at the victory of Salamis'. The possibilities of altering the design were extremely limited: it had been open to dissenters now for four years to challenge any aspect of John Coates's work, but no one had convincingly done so. His ship was a professional, scientific design which accorded with all known evidence, and was intended to meet clear criteria of performance.

It was precisely because the Marsala ship's tenons were found to be inadequate on testing that John Coates had made sure that ours would meet the demands imposed upon them. It was perfectly true that some deviations from ancient practice had been judged inevitable, and all these had been duly noted in an article published in *Antiquity* in March 1987. Timber of the quality used in ancient times was now difficult to come by if the botanically correct species were used. In their place, as has been said, Douglas fir had been employed for the planking, iroko for the keel, stem and stern, and hull stiffeners, and live oak for the tenons. These substitutions were effected after consultation with botanists and timber specialists, and can have had only the most minimal effect on performance. Then, in order to protect the investment of work and money in the ship, modern preservatives were used. The question of caulking was shelved altogether, and the seams sealed with an entirely modern two-part polysulphide elastomer: likewise the best modern underwater paints were used, and all timbers treated with preservative. Not so to do would, in our view, have been absurd antiquarianism. Similarly, modern navigation lights and anchors were provided.

The methods of construction were those used in antiquity, although power hand-tools were employed where necessary and additional frames provided to act as a guide to the workmen. None of these deliberate departures from authenticity should have detracted from the accuracy of

Fig. 50 Rosie Randolph

our reconstruction, but, as we have seen, the builders contrived some unintentional, and more serious, errors. Nevertheless, if our ship did perform at sea as well as we hoped, it would be difficult indeed for anyone to deny that it differed significantly from the ancient trireme – not that any such difficulty stopped academics from questioning what apparently seemed to them a juvenile exercise. With some virtuous exceptions, archaeologists too often believe that while brushing dust off potsherds is a laudable function of scholarship, testing theories against reality is nothing more than schoolboyish adventurism.

As well as explaining our intention to a sometimes still sceptical audience, John Morrison had to superintend the organization of the sea trials. Among the most notable of the oarsmen whose enthusiasm had been stimulated by the exhibition of the trial piece at Henley was Boris Rankov, who for successive years had rowed in the victorious Oxford Blue Boat. As well as being a distinguished oarsman, Boris is also a classical scholar and he found the trireme much to his taste. He volunteered to act as pulling master and to prepare a plan for the trials.

Some 200 other volunteers had also come forward: we accepted them all. In retrospect this may have been misjudged, since the only common qualifications our oars possessed were enthusiasm and the ability to pay the fare. We took women as well as men, schoolboys and grandfathers, light-weights and hulks. There is no doubt that a more balanced crew would have been able to perform better – probably much better – but being enthusiasts ourselves we could hardly resist the same quality in others.

Henley had also brought us an invaluable acquisition in the shape of Rosie Randolph (fig. 50), who not only arranged fund-raising events, but took on responsibility for organizing the transport and housing of the trial crew: a task which turned out to be well-nigh Herculean in the face of constant alterations of plan.

If we were to be able to make arrangements for the crew and friends (now more than 200 of them) who wanted to be present at the trials, or allow them to make their own arrangements, we needed to be able to fix the date of the trials some time ahead. Since the majority were either students or teachers, they could only make themselves available in either the spring or summer vacations. Had the revised completion date of January '87 been met we might have been able to hold trials in April, since once Tsakakos had finished three months more would be needed for the naval dockyard to do its work. This would include swamp and stability tests, fitting-out, rigging, and training a Greek deck crew in the techniques of handling a trireme.

Then, following the sea trials to be carried out by our volunteer crew, the ship would formally be received into the Hellenic Navy. Until that time our trireme would remain nameless; the launching ceremony would not, as is the practice with merchant ships, also be a christening. We had proffered some suggestions as to a future name, culled from the recorded names of historic vessels – *Nike, Aphrodisia, Demokratia, Gnome* – but it would be the Navy's privilege to choose.

But January 1987 found the ship still far from finished. John Coates continued commuting between Bath and Keratsini, where he was now happy to see six men at work and significant progress being made. No new revised completion date had (probably wisely) been agreed, but he judged that the whole might be completed by May, which, while ruling out the possibility of trials being held in the spring, did offer a reasonable prospect for later in the year. A further visit in April indicated that this might not be unduly optimistic. True, the work was not altogether finished, but little, seemingly,

remained to be done. The shed was fully occupied by the ship, with the shelter deck nearly all in place and the seats and stretchers fixed (fig. 51). The ancillary items – spars, sails, and oars – were reported to be ready at the sub-contractors.

For the first time, feeling reasonably certain that we would have a ship that summer, I went to the island of Spetse, to see the spot where the *Argo* had been built.

The site of the *Argo*'s building lies in a pleasant cove a mile or so distant from the main harbour, overlooked by a church which claims some renown for once having held, for a few weeks, the pickled body of Paul Bonaparte, son of Napoleon's brother Lucien, who died in fighting for Greek independence. Several small boatyards have space on the beach, among them that of Vasilis Delimitros, the taciturn and remarkable builder of the *Argo*, but all had been too small for our purposes. None could have provided a sufficiently level expanse to accommodate the trireme. Spetse, although it approximated closely enough to our original fantasies of a sun-drenched island, is also inconveniently far removed from any centre of industry, and the extended line-of-communications needed to build there would have added to the difficulties of supervision.

It was, nevertheless, interesting to see traditional boat-builders at work. Construction there seemed to be a matter of skill and experience: the qualities needed by fishing boats were well understood and faithfully built, by hand, into the sturdy craft that lined the harbours. Vasilis, who had visited Keratsini, was caustic about the length of time Tsakakos was taking and clearly thought he could have done a better job himself. He had certainly produced a good boat for Tim Severin, but what I saw on a brief visit convinced me that Spetse, charming though it is, could never have offered a practical alternative to Keratsini.

Later that month Spiros Mercouris was able to give us a firm date for the commissioning – 15 August 1987.

August had disadvantages in terms of the availability of flights and places to stay; it is a month when the brisk northerly winds, the Meltemene, are common, and it would be inconveniently hot; but these defects were compensated for by Boris Rankov's being able to be there at that time. He had taken up a new appointment at the University of Western Australia

Fig. 51 Work progresses: thalamian oar, showing sleeve to keep out water

in Perth, and had found that a later date would clash with the start of his term.

Boris is more than a successful oarsman. He possesses that ability to generate a feeling of confidence in a crew that enables them to put forward their finest concerted effort. With our heterogeneous crew this would be essential if we were even to approach optimum performance.

Rosie Randolph then settled down to the business of arranging flights and beds for families and friends with the help of Alastair Green, a recent graduate in classical studies from Durham, who had offered his services as our administrator. We planned to get our crew out two weeks before the commissioning and hoped to have them trained well enough to perform creditably in public on that important day, which happens to be the Feast of the Assumption. In view of the different meanings of that word, it seemed an apt choice. We were assuming that John Morrison's theory of the oar arrangement worked when 170 people attempted to row together; that John Coates's design was stable, seaworthy and would not need substantial modifications; and, most importantly, that the ship would in fact be completed on time.

In the absence of any reliable completion date, we worked backwards from the one fixed point we had, that of 15 August, which gave a starting date of 1 August for sea trials. In the period between completion (a date still unknown) and 1 August the naval dockyards had to receive the ship, train a deck crew, fit her out, and make any alterations they felt necessary. (All this, to which we had originally allotted three months, had eventually to be compressed into six weeks.)

On 20 June we were told that trireme would be ready for launching on the following Saturday, the 27th. This found John Coates already at Keratsini, as indeed he had been for many days previously, occupied once more by the continuing problem of the hypozoma.

Just as had happened in ancient times, the hypozoma had to be rigged immediately before the launch when all the other work was finished. The delayed programme now allowed John only a week to deal with this intractable object, and it proved to be too short a time. Polyester rope, which John had finally chosen and included in the original specification, proved impossible to obtain in Greece, and a replacement filament polypropylene was used. The eventual design had the hypozoma slung just below the zygian beams, using two loops of rope led round a vertical member in the bows and a horizontal one in the stern (fig. 39). Midships, just aft of the mast, Dorian Dymoke's tightening device was to act upon both loops.

John had already found the analysis of the behaviour of ropes a complex affair on his model: the real thing, where a pressure of 20 tons was looked for, proved even more difficult. When the hypozomata were fitted and tightened, the pressure on the posts at the stem and stern was too great to permit the ropes to slip round. Oil, mutton fat, grease and persuasion were applied, but in vain: when the tensioning gear was brought into play,

Fig. 52 The chain hypozoma which John Coates was forced to use in place of ropes

instead of tightening the rope it just propelled itself forward until it slapped up against the next beam. Unable to find an answer, and pressed for time, John had to content himself with stretching a wire rope between the anchor posts, tightened to a load of only 12 tons. This was hardly authentic, but would at least fulfil the hypozoma's function until more research on the arcane questions of tension and torsion in ropes could be done; for practical purposes the substitution made little difference, since the effectiveness of the hypozoma depends only on the position in which it is placed and the tension at which it is held. But for the moment, at any rate, we had to give the wretched rope best (fig. 52).

On the evening of 27 June the trireme made her first journey, from the shed to the dockside, a distance of perhaps 300 yards. The first part of this operation entailed shifting the hull from its chocks to the trolleys

Fig. 53 The Tsakakos shed partly demolished to allow the trireme out

and burning away the supports with oxy-acetylene torches – a process not without dangers. Then the roof and one end of the ship shed had to be removed to let her be inched out into the open (fig. 53). Maureen Green, observing for the *Smithsonian* magazine, thought that the slow emergence of the ship from the ruins of the shed in which she had been built resembled nothing more closely than a gorgeous butterfly breaking out of its chrysalis.

For the first time now the ship could be seen as a whole, since in the shed it was impossible to get more than a few feet away. It was indeed a transformation. From being a collection of mechanical problems she had become an integrated work of compelling form. Her curved stern swept up like the tail of a scorpion and the regular vertical rhythm of ports lent a malevolent power to the wicked sharpness of the golden-bronze ram.

The hull above the waterline had been treated only with clear preservative, leaving the timber its natural colour; below she was black, which served to point up how small the wetted surface actually would be. The trireme's only colour was right forward where the ram was surmounted by the traditional painted eyes. The character these gave to the hull was indefinably powerful; aggression, wariness, and instant readiness. The trireme lay in her cradle like some great sea-creature, quiescent for the moment but packed with latent power.

As this was the first time the hull had been unsupported, John Coates watched, with some concern and the defective joints much in mind, for any evidence of flexing. All seemed well, however, and the slow journey to the water's edge was uneventful.

Saturday's launch had, at short notice and decidedly against John Coates's own preference, been made into something of an occasion. It was a hot, dusty morning, and a number of disparate emotions were discernible among the gathering. John had his worries about his ship surviving her ordeal and then floating at the right depth. Demetrios Tsakakos, if he had any such concern, had lost it in the excitement of what might well have been the greatest day of his life, when he was the centre of attention. His workers were proud of their achievement but sad to see their ship go. For their part the Navy were only anxious to get their much-delayed trireme away from the yard and into their own care for its abbreviated fitting-out period. Overlying these individual concerns was a general exhilaration at having seen something really important through to a finish.

All our Greek friends were there – Anastasias Tzamtzis and Admiral Makris, who had been the first to offer encouragement; Harry Tzalas and George Dracopoulous, who had done so much else for the cause of maritime history; Kolliniatis and Stavros Platis from the Hellenic Navy; and Colin McGregor from the Royal Navy. Spiros Mercouris presided over the occasion. Only the venerable figure of John Morrison was absent.

The trireme was now aligned alongside the dock in her cradle, but tethered by slings to a floating crane. With no masts, spars, fittings or oars, the naked hull looked more than ever like a giant fish caught in a net. When the crane lifted her, the whole of her weight would be taken by these slings which had been placed over the outriggers rather than close against the hull. The whole strain would therefore be borne by that relatively weak beam; if it failed, an almighty crack would follow, the whole ship would drop six inches in its sling, and there would be a great deal of work for the Salamis dockyard.

At least, however, damage to the outriggers could be repaired. More worrying was the thought that the whole business would strain those joints under the waterline that had initially been too loosely secured and then filled up with glue by a repentant Tsakakos.

The waterfront at Keratsini is a thoroughly unsuitable setting for so rare an event. Decayed fencing surrounds a patch of windswept concrete on which a platform had been erected, its structure of scaffolding poles

Fig. 54 The launch

unconcealed. The wine-dark sea is mustard-murky, and the site of Xerxes' throne, wherever exactly it was, is concealed by acres of shabby housing.

The ceremonies proved at least so far efficacious as to preserve the ship from immediate danger (fig. 55). After appropriate prayers, speeches and hymns, a flight of doves was released from the deck and a bottle of champagne broken on the ram. These two symbols, respectively recalling the Biblical flood and the libation to Poseidon, neatly summarized both the way in which the trireme straddled the two and half millennia since the time of Themistocles, and the continuity of maritime traditions.

There was silence – not a usual event in Greece – as the crane slowly raised the hull from its trolley and swung it through 90 degrees towards the water (fig. 54). Twenty feet in the air, the resemblance to some gigantic missile poised for hurling at the enemy was predominant. A minute later and she was, for the first time, floating serenely on the turgid waters of the Aegean.

Fig. 55 Priests (centre) pray on the quayside as the crowd looks on

There were cheers, applause and a rush to view the ship. Dimitrios Tsakakos, damply delighted, was the first to sit in the trierarch's chair. But John Coates had found a dinghy and was being sculled round the ship, checking her level in the water. I called out to him rather nervously, but could see from his expression that it was, as I should have known, exactly right. The depth markers registered 0.85 m forward and 0.9 m aft, almost precisely what John had calculated. The fitting-out could go ahead. John, for once a little elevated, was borne off by Captain McGregor to lunch at the Yacht Club.

8

Alarms and excursions

W ITH the hull afloat and safe in the capable hands of the Hellenic Navy, and having, as we thought, finalized arrangements for the trials, we should have been able to relax and perfect our plans for observing and measuring the ship's performance. Instead we found ourselves energetically engaged on another front. The reason that John Morrison had not been present at the launch was that both he and Rosie Randolph had only just returned from a strenuous week in Athens.

A couple of weeks before the launch we had been told that the trials would be held not in Poros but Piraeus, and that commissioning would be on 9, not 15, August. This was an unwelcome idea indeed. If there is one place in Greece not to spend a fortnight, Piraeus must be it: no bathing for miles, few inexpensive tavernas, and a great deal of commercial bustle. The harbour where the trireme would be based is tremendously congested and, at least in the first days, an untrained crew would be faced with many hazards. John Morrison and Rosie Randolph, in some alarm, lost no time in getting to Athens in order to argue the case for Poros and 15 August.

On their arrival they found the Hellenic Navy to be as surprised as we had been at the alteration, and the original date was quickly reinstated. What was more, the Hellenic Navy, with their unvarying generosity, agreed that we might have the trials at Poros and accommodate the trial crew in the Naval School. We were then able to swing into action, confirm more than 200 air tickets, and make arrangements for additional rooms in Poros to house more than 100 family and friends. From my now numerous visits to the island, I could assure them of the existence of those amenities that make Greek holidays so pleasurable, and of a warm welcome from the Poriotes, who were delighted that their island had been chosen for an event appealing so strongly to Greek historical instincts.

But then followed a more serious difficulty. We heard that the commissioning date was to be postponed from 15 to 23 August. From this there was to be no appeal, it being a matter beyond the Navy's control. Could we arrange for the crew to stay on? The Navy were happy to extend their hospitality for that period. There were now only four weeks to go before the crew were due to arrive, and Rosie found herself telephoning all those she could find, explaining the situation, and re-negotiating flights and rooms. As well as the families and friends of the crew, some forty others had signed up for a week's holiday which would have included the finish of the trials and the commissioning. There was nothing we could do about that, but more than 100 of the crew were able to make arrangements to stay on for an extra week. The spare places would be filled by Greek oarsmen who would have only six days of training – the rest were needed for the movement of the trireme from Poros to Piraeus. This would be hardly enough to master the techniques, but we felt that the original crew could probably provide enough stiffening.

The third shock came as we actually arrived at Poros and learned that the commissioning was to be postponed once more, to the 26th, apparently because the Prime Minister Mr Papandreou wished to attend the ceremony. The effect of this alteration so late in the proceedings, was drastic. Most of the 100 oarsmen who had agreed to stay on for an extra week could not alter their plans again to extend their stay for another three days. Only fifteen of them were able to do this and form a nucleus for what would have to be a scratch commissioning crew. Rosie had once more to start re-booking flights and accommodation.

Some other troubling portents appeared. The last days of July found Greece experiencing the most damaging heatwave of modern times. Temperatures rose to 122° on the inland plains, to 107° in Athens itself, and stayed in the 100s for days on end. People began to die in scores, especially the old but also some of the apparently young and healthy. Mortuaries and graveyards were unable to cope: bodies lay in hospital wards or were stacked in refrigerated railway wagons. Horror stories abounded.

I had driven from England to Greece through Eastern Europe with Tony Bennett, an old Cambridge friend, arriving in Athens on the Saturday before the trials were due to start. It was a deserted city. Everyone able to leave had made for the coast; those who had to stay remained indoors during the day, only venturing out in the evening when the thermometer dropped to a mere 95°. If this sort of thing had continued, trials would have been impossible. No crew, fresh from an unusually cool English summer, could have been expected to row in such conditions, cooped up in the confined space of a trireme's hull. It was as much as a reasonably fit person could do to walk about quite slowly and seek the shade.

Fortunately, temperatures abated somewhat later that week, though the Greek summer had given a taste of its quality; August, we had always known, was the worst possible time to attempt trials, but we were committed to it.

Then came another blow: we had fixed on August, in spite of its disadvantages, because Boris Rankov, who as pulling master would be the key figure in the trials, had to be back in Australia for the beginning of the new term. Now we learned that he had suffered a spinal injury and was stretched helpless on his bed. The gloom that this news cast was alleviated by the information that Boris would not be out of action for too long, and that he had already committed his plans for the trials to paper. These would be supplemented by the presence, initially, of Dan Topolski who had coached twelve Oxford Blue crews to victory. Dan had seen the trial piece in action at Henley and understood the changes in technique that the oarsmen would need to learn: most of the crew had some experience of rowing on a sliding seat, but this would be of little advantage in the different circumstances of the trireme.

The programme for the trials was restricted by the limitations of the time available to us. A longer period would have been much better, but many of the crew could not spare more than fifteen days. We decided that no more than two outings a day, of two hours each, would be practicable, except for a final day's long row. To escape the worst of the August heat these would be in the early morning and in the last hours of daylight. Five half-days would be set aside for sailing and rest, which left forty-six hours of rowing in which to put the ship through her paces. Starting with so elementary a matter as embarkation drill, the crew would proceed to learn how to co-ordinate the handling of the oars before trying such simple manœuvres as casting off and mooring, turning under oar, and finally pacing over time and distance. To many people, co-ordination looked more of a problem than we had found it to be at Henley. Although there is very little space indeed between the blades in the water, the oarsmen in the trial piece had not found it too difficult to strike a rhythm. However we were very conscious of the fact that 170 people striking out at sea is a very different matter from fifteen firmly moored outside the Leander Club, and that any failure on the part of the oarsmen to act together could have serious results.

Given the limitations of time there could be no question of trying this summer to emulate any of the long classical passages. That would have to wait until next year, or later. After the lapse of so many centuries we could not expect to master the old techniques too rapidly, and several trial programmes would probably be needed to test the ship fully. Our main aim now was to see whether John Coates's design could hope to match the speed and manœuvrability that were characteristic of the Salamis trireme, or whether as Eric Leach, had prophesied, it would be: '. . . a one second folly: the splash of oars, a furrow ploughed, a clattering of blades and a splintering: a stunning silence; disenchantment.' There were still many who might agree with Mr Leach.

After the launch John Coates had accompanied the trireme to Salamis dockyard to help the Navy deal with any alterations or adjustments that might be necessary. These were apparently done with alacrity, and there was even time to muster a scratch crew to row the ship for short distances: but we never discovered whether the stability tests had been carried out. We would have to find that out the experimental, hard, way. But whatever had needed to be done was done, and on Thursday 30 July the trireme, having been towed from Piraeus, docked at Poros to await the arrival of the trials crew.

As well as planning the trials themselves, Boris Rankov had established a policy for placing the oarsmen in the ship. One obvious practical method would have been to do this by size and weight – taller ones in the thranite (top tier), shorter in the thalamian (bottom), and middlers in the zygian – but Boris had applied his successful experience in racing eights to developing a different system. Appreciating the vital importance of co-ordination, he had followed Groucho Marx's dictum that 'nothing propinqs like propinquity', and placed those who had rowed together near their friends, believing that this would enable them to adapt more easily to each other's style. Given the quite extraordinarily varied crew we had acquired, this turned out to be a wise decision.

Exactly how heterogeneous a crew it was became immediately clear when the ferry from Piraeus docked at Poros on Friday 31 July, disgorging some 150 oarsmen and oarswomen. Long thin schoolboys, muscular young Adonises, plump little girls, white-haired veterans, and hard, experienced oarsmen; the tallest 6′ 5″ and a bit, the shortest 4′ 11″; the oldest fifty-nine, the youngest sixteen. There were research scientists, policemen, GPs, QCs, professors, shopkeepers, the Secretary of the Royal Commission on Historical Monuments, bank managers, company directors, and students of most subjects, relevant and irrelevant – all excited and enthusiastic. Their costumes included decaying jeans, sarongs, halter tops, trireme T-shirts, and others with legends of varying impropriety. Boris had warned that working from a fixed seat, even with a cushion, would be hard on the behind, and had advised that rowing shorts should be reinforced. The preferred method, it was now made clear by a parade of variegated bottoms, was to sew on beer mats (fig. 56). As these strode, ambled and bobbed towards the barracks, announcing the merits of different breweries – Benskins, and Greene King being favourites – an anthropologist could have foretold that we were about to experience the phenomenon known as culture shock.

The Hellenic Navy Petty Officer School (SYMN) is a school for boys between the ages of fifteen and nineteen who hope to become petty officers in the Hellenic Navy. They are instructed in the usual school subjects, and such naval topics as basic navigation and boat-handling. A number of whalers and dinghies, as well as tubs and shells, are kept for this purpose. The families of the instructors live in a separate block, opposite the main gate and behind a children's playground. A pair of World War II two-pound anti-tank guns decorate the main entrance, and an ancient 4″ gun points out over the straits to Galatas. In spite of this lack of aggressive intent or capability, the SYMN is officially as much a naval station as any NATO Polaris submarine base.

The Trust organizers had appreciated this and made their own arrangements for discipline. Passes, with photographs and passport numbers, had been prepared and distributed to all (or almost all, for we were to find some notable omissions) participants. Eleven barrack-masters worked a shift system to ensure that one senior representative was always on base. Room presidents were to be elected to take responsibility for good order in their barrack-rooms and to agree cleaning rotas. We felt, correctly as it turned out, that such a system would work best, and that anything more regimented would only provoke derision.

But navies have their little ways, and the Hellenic Navy had worked out its own system. As our vagabondish collection of oars straggled towards the base, guarded by armed sentries crisp in summer whites, some grinding of cogs was inevitable. Naval control involved changing the trireme pass

Fig. 56 The crew arrives, with rowing shorts reinforced as advised

for a naval pass every time anyone entered the base, and vice versa on exit. Looking at the number, and appreciating the disposition, of our crew, we could foresee that this would rapidly prove unworkable.

The accommodation itself was as neatly arranged as everything else in the school. We had been given a two-storey barrack to ourselves, well provided with hot showers, divided into smaller rooms, and all newly decorated. Not only the oarsmen and women but the official observers, including John Coates, took up residence there. Even those who had never sampled this sort of communal life were impressed, but the Navy system remained to be coped with.

On the first hot Friday afternoon it took two and a half hours to sort out the documentation. The programme had called for the Friday evening to be spent explaining the ship to the crew, and showing them around her in small parties. But no one was allowed on the trireme unless the Hellenic Naval commander was on board, and he was nowhere to be found. Even John Morrison, when he ascended the gangplank, was ordered off by an embarrassed sentry and the evening's programme had to be abandoned. All that could be done was to admire the ship, frustratedly, from the quay.

It was the first time anyone there other than John Coates and I had seen the trireme on the water, and even in the month since the launch she had undergone a remarkable change. Previously she had been incomplete, caught in the metamorphosis between structure and ship, between being a collection of timbers and the warship complete, self-sufficient and armed, which she now was. Not that she looked particularly aggressive, lying stern to, her beak facing out into the bay, and Tsakakos's beautiful curved timbers rising smoothly to the spreading *aphlaston* from which flew the Greek national flag. Her masts were rigged – the boat mast, shorter and inclining forward; the main mast solid and upright. All her oars were neatly stowed, only the white spoons projecting from their ports: wide for the thranites, long and slim for the thalamians, and the zygian shapes somewhere in between. Her massive steering oars, each as thick as a telegraph pole and controlled by iron-bound tillers, were in place. Riding lightly on the water she seemed ready for anything: provided, that was, she had a crew (fig. 57).

There was, however, one obvious defect. The suspect joints had failed, to some extent at least, and she was visibly hogging. It was not much – some 5 cms, or about 2 inches at either end – but enough to impart a discernible curve to her gunwale and deck. While annoying, this was not too important, since it would not affect her performance and could probably be rectified during the winter refit, when the hypozomata could be tightened to their designed load.

The expected crunch duly came the next morning. We had scheduled an early start at 6.15 to 6.30, with breakfast available from 5.30. This meal could not be provided in the barracks, and we had arranged for it to be taken at a nearby hotel. Under the system of passes we had devised this should have gone smoothly enough; showing a pass to the sentry on returning ought have been all that was needed. But with 170 people having to wait for up to fifteen minutes while the harassed guards collected one set of passes, matched pass against pass and face against photograph, and issued the second pass, repeating the whole operation on the crew's return, a certain

Fig. 57 The trireme berthed at Poros and waiting for her crew

amount of noise and discontent became audible. Complaints started flowing from the officers' wives and children housed opposite and awakened at what was, even for Greece, an uncomfortably early hour.

With everyone returned from breakfast we started our boarding arrangements at 6.30. We knew that a clear system was necessary for safe embarkation, the restricted space on board making it essential that each rower took his place in turn, boarding from the stern, the thranite bow oars first, ending up with the thalamian strokes. A grid had been drawn up to make this easier, with each person being allocated a number and a place. The grid was reproduced full-scale on the quay in front of the ship, where the crew took up their proper places before each outing. This system also made it easier to identify any absent from parade, and to find replacements from reserves, as well as to organize any changes that might be suggested. It had been introduced by one of our volunteers, Peter McLeod, an instructor at the Coventry Police School, who had pointed out that police had to be instructed even in the art of getting on and off buses quickly, and that in a much larger – and inherently unstable – object like a ship the difficulties would be aggravated. Peter's suggestion was not only accepted but he was appointed as crew manager, responsible for discipline, for which his police training and brisk air of command well suited him. Without someone of Peter's character in command the next two weeks would have been much more painful than they turned out to be.

Boris Rankov's role as pulling master was taken at the last minute by Mike Budd, a GP from Hereford who had originally joined as our medical officer (fig. 58). He continued in that dual capacity until joined by Peter McLeod's brother Jamie, fresh from a tour in Papua New Guinea. As medical officer his first advice to the crew was brisk: 'People get upset tummies abroad by getting too hot, not just by drinking the water and eating the food. Stick to freshly cooked food, and keep out of the sun altogether in the middle of the day. I'm not going to have anyone with the squitters on this ship. There's nowhere to go, anyway.'

As pulling master he would have been known in ancient Greece as the *keleustes*: his responsibility was to encourage, persuade and cajole the oarsmen into giving their best. A ship with a good *keleustes* could make a passage twice as quickly as one badly officered, and Xenophon describes a good *keleustes* as one whose men 'come ashore sweating and congratulating each other', while those working under a bad one 'come in cold, hating their foreman and hated by him'.

Although *keleustes* is often translated as boatswain or bo'sun, a more illuminating modern analogy might be with a chief engineer, not concerned with navigation or manœuvres but with keeping the propulsion unit in first-class order, the important difference being that the *keleustes* relied on human beings and therefore worked as does the cox of a racing eight. Mike Budd made a wonderful job of both aspects of the task; as a medical man he took good care of his crew, and knew how much could reasonably – and occasionally unreasonably – be expected of them, while as a cox he knew all the arts of command and persuasion. His stocky figure, invariably topped by a bright red sun hat, was instantly recognizable, usually surrounded by oarsmen trying to persuade him to try out one of their pet theories. So enthu-

Fig. 58 Left – Mike Budd, keleustes; right – Tim Shaw, kubernetes

siastic were crew that ideas and discussions flowed day and night; in every café and taverna voices were raised, causing John Morrison to remark, when once things got a little too heated: 'Even the youngest of us may sometimes be wrong.'

The second senior officer was the *kubernetes* or helmsman, equivalent perhaps to the 'master' of a Georgian Royal Navy ship, as the warrant officer in charge of navigation was then known. His importance is reflected in the title itself, for *kubernetes* is equivalent to the Latin *gubernator* and English *governor*. He sat immediately in front of the trierarch, and operated the twin steering oars. The essential qualities for a helmsman are calmness and alacrity. Our *kubernetes*, Tim Shaw, had these in abundance: even if a sign of agitation had crossed his countenance it would have been invisible, since only his nose could be seen between beard, sunglasses and sun visor. Tall for a cox, Tim had nevertheless coxed the Queen's College, Oxford boat, and reached the Thames Challenge cup at Henley (fig. 58).

These two officers reported to the trierarch, or captain. An Athenian trierarch had to be a man of some status, originally having a house and land, legitimate children, and being under 50 years old. Although the ship was provided for him, and in theory the wages and expenses were paid, he was personally responsible for keeping his trireme in commission, and

Fig. 59 Lieutenant Papadas (left)

Fig. 60 The crew lines up on the grid (right)

therefore needed to be reasonably rich. The trierarchy came to be regarded as a convenient way of raising tax revenue. A wealthy man would be appointed trierarch and expected to pay all expenses, but allowed to delegate actual command of the ship, rather in the same way that eighteenth-century English noblemen raised regiments of yeomanry and militia.

Our own trierarch, Lieutenant Dimitri Papadas, was made responsible for the safety of the ship by the Greek Navy, and was in direct command. He had taken over when the ship was at Salamis and supervised the dockyard work done there. A trim, neat man, with a Captain Kettle beard, he has something of Kettle's acerbity (fig. 59). Though expressing himself forcefully in Greek, the Lieutenant had no English, which we thought might prove something of an impediment to communication.

And so it seemed. At 6.30 on Saturday morning, 1 August, 170 crew

stood drawn up in six lines, port and starboard, thranites, zygians, and thalamians, each in his appointed place, hungrily eyeing the forbidden trireme which floated a few yards off, guarded by a Greek seaman (fig. 60). A hundred and seventy men and women drawn up in a block make an impressive array of bodies, equal to four bus-loads or a full infantry company. It looked impossible that they should ever fit into the space available in the slim hull. We knew from working the trial piece, that it could be done, but fifteen squashed people generate much less anguish and discomfort than 170. There were also forty or so deck officers, observers and reserves on parade, and all waiting for Lieutenant Papadas, who alone could allow the day's work to start. But the Lieutenant did not show up.

At 7 Mike Budd dismissed the crew, asking them to re-assemble at 7.30, while we decided what should be done. I had already had a little trouble with the authorities a couple of days before, since it appeared that I had not been given a pass, and the unfortunate young conscript who nevertheless let me in was given five days CB for his pains. John Coates had at that time explained to me, from his long experience of service ways, the necessity of working with the system and the inadvisability of making a fuss; but on this occasion I felt a fuss was essential. Rosie, both Johns and I marched off to have it out with the barrack commander.

We found him, with the trierarch, peacefully drinking coffee. There had been, it appeared, a misunderstanding, and Lieutenant Papadas did not realize that his presence was required. But at 7.30 we were assured we would have our trierarch and would be able to begin the sea trials. Mike prevailed upon the less ruly members of the crew to avoid any demonstration of their discontent, and only slightly later than the newly appointed time we were able to start the embarkation.

All in all, it had not been the best beginning to the trials, and matters did not immediately improve. With only one gangplank, boarding took a good fifteen minutes, as the crew found their ways into sometimes very cramped seats. The restricted space, unaccustomed angles and heavy oars

Fig. 61 Rowing with one level of oars only

caused consternation in some quarters, especially among those who had been trained in racing shells with plenty of room for a long reach. As an illustration of the different conditions it might be noted that a trireme with a maximum of thirty-one oar places fore and aft is only twice as long as a racing shell with eight places. Those few of our crew who had had experience of pulling heavier craft at sea found things somewhat easier.

Knowing that this would be so, Mike Budd had evolved a system of section leaders. The ship was divided into six sections – fore, midships, and aft, on both port and starboard: blue, green, red; white, black and yellow. Each section was headed by an experienced oarsman who watched over some thirty rowers. He had to observe their performance, give coaching, advise on changes, clear any tangles that might arise, and effect running repairs: this last turned out to be a demanding job, as defects of workmanship began to show in service.

With these divisions, the ship could theoretically be rowed in many different ways – each level of oars could be used separately, or any two levels in combination; or one half, one third, or two thirds fore and aft. In practice we discovered that the best combinations were thranites only, all together, or either half fore or aft.

The team leaders were as varied a collection as the crew themselves. Colin 'Cocky' Cox is an Oxford boatman; Brian Johnson owns shops selling rowing equipment; Andrew Ruddle is a City bank manager. With the irrepressible Pete Thomson, Mike Wilmot, Stephen Walter and Stephen Sprowart, they collectively brought a couple of centuries' rowing experience to bear on coaching, encouraging and co-ordinating the crew. Any success we might have would depend upon their vigilance and powers of leadership.

Casting off for the first time, we ran straight into trouble. The trierarch gave operating orders in Greek, translated into English for the benefit of the *keleustes* and *kubernetes*. They in turn gave commands to the rowers and operated the steering oars, respectively. In ancient times the first command to be given to the crew was: 'Keep quiet so that you can hear the other orders.' This was soon demonstrated to have been necessary: even in a racing shell with only eight men to control, a cox is given some form of artificial amplification. Controlling 170, even when aided by a megaphone, is an awesome task. Starting from rest was not too difficult, with only the badinage of the crew to overcome, but the noise when under oar, with blades clashing against thole-pins at every stroke, was impressive.

Our first trouble was, however, caused by an excess of prudence. Using

Fig. 62 Rowing with all oars

183

only the aftermost third of the thalamian oars, we crept away from the mooring buoy. The cautious pace did not provide enough forward movement to allow the steering oars to bite, and slowly, inexorably, we drifted into the huge buoy which had once been the mooring for the cruiser *Averoff*. The trierarch and deck crew were too busy fending off the buoy to give the corrective order in time; this would have brought the whole thalamian rank into play and given enough speed to enable the *kubernetes* to steer clear of the obstacle. Although the forward momentum was not great, it was enough to smash one of the oars on impact; fortunately, for otherwise there might have been an injury, the oar was quickly taken inboard. It seemed for a moment as though Eric Leach's prophecy was being fulfilled.

Extricating ourselves from the buoy, we proceeded, using only thranite oars. It was an easy enough task, since with only one level in operation the oarsmen had merely to follow the stroke, as in an overgrown whaler, and we rapidly moved to a good 4 knots. This was heartening, for it proved that we had a fine, easily driven hull; but it was hardly relevant to the real task. We had not set out to build a pentecontor (although that would itself have been a rewarding project: such a beautiful boat would have taught us much about even more ancient techniques, would have looked almost as impressive, and been a very great deal easier to design!). Our aim from the time of that first dinner party had been finally to crack the trireme conundrum, and to do that we had to see that the ship could move quickly and effectively using all three levels of oars. What we had at the moment was a pretty pentecontor, rowing smoothly and well, but carrying at least another 120 idlers as ballast.

When we brought them all into action for the first time, however, the results were less happy. The thalamians and zygians were rowing blind: only the thranites could see what was actually happening to their oars, and the others had to follow as best they could. Even when setting the most leisurely of strokes there was a clash of oars, and the occasional undeniable splinter. The same phenomenon had occurred when the mock-up and the trial piece were first tested. A strong thalamian oar, finding that his level above the water and the angle of his blade approximated to that of a conventional shell, would take a good long stroke: an adjacent zygian, working at a less familiar angle, would essay an apprehensive dab. Their blades would cross, clash, and perhaps jam. On jamming, the inboard end of one oar might well catch the head of the oarsman quite sharply between it and the beam behind him. The thranites did their best to keep clear of what was going on underneath them, at the same time as trying to make a good powerful stroke, but at times they were reduced to waving their blades ineffectually in the air.

The thranites' advantage of being able to see what they were doing was the only one they had. Even the reduced angle of their oars was still more than 30°; they found the position uncomfortable, and the heavy oars needed considerable strength to push down into the water. Conditions had been different when rowing the trial piece at Henley: since it was moored to the towpath no one needed to exert full force, in fact we had had to discourage those who did. Now, moving the ship forward with 170 differently sized and shaped oarsmen, all with a wide range of experience and rowing with different degrees of enthusiasm, poor co-ordination was much more noticeable.

We regained our moorings under thranite oars only, and settled down to analyse what had gone wrong and propose improvements. Opinions differed both as to the gravity of the matter and to the possible solutions. Those of us who had seen the trial piece in action were confident that with practice co-ordination would develop, although whether sufficient power to push the ship to anywhere near her design limits would be generated was a very different thing. Others, whose rowing experience had been all on sliding seats, were gloomier. Complaints that the seats were too close together were heard from those persons who had not done their homework properly. John Morrison and John Coates had generously arranged for copies of their book *The Athenian Trireme* to be given to all of the volunteers, but some certainly had not benefited from its study and had failed to realize the impossibility of providing any more space.

Although the first Saturday's discussions were probably the most productive, every outing was followed by an analysis of the performance by the officers and section leaders, supplemented by a suggestion box and numerous interminable discussions at Poros's hospitable bars and tavernas. If the steady internal application of beer and ouzo could improve the trireme's performance, its success would be guaranteed.

The first, sober decisions on what needed to be done benefited from Dan Topolski's presence. He had been able to observe something of the preliminary testing while the ship was in Salamis dockyard, and had formed his views on possible improvements. With some reluctance the very smallest members of the crew were dropped, since they just could not manage to handle the heavy oars. We had always felt that 5′ 4″ was a sensible minimum, and Erica Cox and Sharon Bowley, for example, only just reached 5'. But those two cheerful girls happily accepted such mundane tasks as melting mutton fat to grease the cushions and oar straps (although authentic, this appalled Lieutenant Papadas, who, when confronted with the melted fat, would not permit its use), and contributed much to general jollity of the fortnight.

A major improvement was made possible by Peter McLeod's recommendation that the thranites should make full use of the visibility their position afforded them to keep the zygian and thalamian blades from striking each other. To do this they had to place their oars very precisely in the limited patch of water available to them, and leave the spoon in the water for long enough to keep the others apart (fig. 63). That way there might be the odd tap, but the undignified and dangerous knitting that we had previously seen was prevented. Some of those who had rowed the trial piece confirmed later that they had adopted a similar method. The noise problem was overcome to some extent by stationing a sub-*keleustes* at the main mast, also with a megaphone, to relay commands to the forward half of the ship.

For their part, the naval school command, having recovered from what must have been the nasty shock of seeing our motley and independent crew invade their nice orderly barracks, reacted wonderfully. Lieutenant Commander Papaisidoru and Lieutenant Loukas Souchlas were present at every start, and did all they could to oblige us. Breakfasters were allowed to come and go freely; the pass system was simplified. Some unattached Navy men took advantage of the presence of girls to improve their English. And, perhaps most importantly, Simon Zafet's services were put at our disposal.

Greece has universal national service in the armed forces, as Britain used to do. While the advantages of this to the conscripts or the services is debatable, it does ensure a constant supply of educated and intelligent young men. Simon, who had taken a Master's Degree in the City of London University, proved himself an admirable ambassador and fixer. Shouts of 'Where's Simon?' and 'Leave it to Simon!' were constantly heard.

From the second day, Sunday, results of the improvements became quickly discernible. We started off with the deck strewn with bodies as the section leaders sprawled, peering over the sides and ordering the blades a little further in- or out-board, so that they formed neat strong lines in the water. And it worked: after the first outing the clashing of oars ceased: all levels pulled steadily together and the ship began to surge through the water. Moving from light to firm pressure she leaped ahead at every stroke.

*Fig. 63 Detail showing how
closely the oar blades come
together in the water*

From a ragged 4 knots she rapidly passed 5, 6 and, on the fourth day, 7 knots. This was far better than we had any right to expect. Our collection of oddments was turning into an able crew, and were well on our way to proving that the Morrison–Coates trireme worked. It was with some confidence that we settled down to putting the ship through her paces for the next ten days.

The first really successful row was on Sunday evening (fig. 64), and as the oars stilled and the Trireme Trust house flag (an Oxford blue ship on a Cambridge blue ground) drooped from the *aphlaston*, John Morrison stood looking contentedly at the fulfilment of his years of study. When he was asked if he felt this to be a very special day for him, he smiled and answered, 'Well, it may have something to do with the sunset, but I *was* feeling rather pleased, actually.'

A typical outing during this period began with the crew gathering on the quay, keeping in the shade of the barracks. Mike Budd would address them briefly on the plan for the outing, and add any reproofs or exhortations he felt necessary ('It's no good complaining you're tired. You should drink less, and get more sleep. You know what your beds are for; use them!') before falling them in on the grid. Once in their seats, casting off was done under thranite oars only, and following the trierarch's orders. Further contretemps with buoys were successfully avoided.

In the waters of the straits, between the Naval School and the open sea, Mike Budd put the ship through time and distance trials. Bearings had been taken from conspicuous objects on the shore, establishing 500 m, 1 and 2 km distances, and timings were taken from these at different rates of striking. Although we got as high a rate as 44 in a sprint, this felt decidedly dangerous, for any missed stroke, broken strap or other incident might result in a very nasty accident as the neighbouring oars smashed into the incapacitated one, jamming the rower's head against the next beam. The gain in speed was not great, and a firm 36–38 was decided upon as the optimum striking rate.

Although straight-line speed was important, the success of the trireme in war depended upon her manœuvrability. The trial programme therefore included simulated war tactics – sharp turns, ramming, recovery and accelerating away. Her quickness in answering the helm proved astonishing. A 90° turn, altering course for an attack, was made within seconds. A 180° turn could be made inside two ship-lengths and one minute. She could simulate a ram by coming to a stop, and shooting off again at an angle with impressive readiness. The heartier members of the crew were anxious to try a real ramming, and one unwary German yacht was greeted with alarmingly realistic klaxon hoots.

From a halt, the trireme could be accelerating through 6 knots, going back the way she had come, within 90 seconds. Speeds and times were recorded by a deck team which included Owain Roberts, the sailing master, Ian Whitehead, a classics scholar who had rowed on the *Argo*, Paul and Marcelle Lippke from Massachusetts, and Graeme Fife. John Ilsley of Bangor was our photographer of record: Tim Watson made the measurement of acceleration and deceleration his own special interest, and devised a complex

Fig. 64 Rowing confidently

instrument fabricated from plastic buckets, lemonade bottles and knotted cord in order to do so. Whatever the results, we were confident that the ship had established, at least for the purpose of the *Guinness Book of Records*, the best recorded times of a trireme under oar.

The crew had found for themselves that the thranites, as well as separating the other oars, should encourage those lower ranks who laboured unseen, dripped on and confined (fig. 65). A deal of amiable banter therefore ensued. Combined with the inevitable noises of the ship, this resulted in such dialogues as:

Mike Budd: 'Easy oars (i.e. stop rowing)' [*Those nearest him do so; those in the bows happily continue, as they are now singing lustily.*]
Mike Budd again: 'Easy oars, for heaven's sake.' [*Bow section carries on rowing.*]
Bow leader, running aft with worried expression: 'What was that Mike? Are you trying to say something? I can't hear a thing when they are singing.'

Fig. 65 Thalamians – 'dripped on and confined'

*Fig. 66 John Coates
checking on details*

Communications between Mike Budd and Lieutenant Papadas were much
improved by the presence of Yannis Manuelides, formerly of Princeton, Chicago, and Clare College, Cambridge, a classical philosopher and member of
the Greek Navy, who acted as instant interpreter and proved an accomplished smoother out of difficulties.

John Coates, conspicuous in a magenta sun hat, was frequently to be
found on board, peering anxiously into recesses, clambering agilely over
obstacles, filling a notebook with observations (fig. 66). John Morrison, still
clinging to his ancient panama, was usually claimed by the journalists, to
each of whom, with his usual grave courtesy, he explained the project for
the *n*th time. Other members of the recording team, were also distinctively
clad: Owain Roberts had found a scarlet cap, Tim Watson a blue one, while
the energetic Paul and Marcelle wore voluminous shorts of imperial
dimensions.

In ancient times the shelter deck and gangways would have accommodated thirty men, of whom twelve were armed marines and the remainder the ship's crew. We were usually able to reproduce these conditions by having visitors supplement deck crew and official observers; most of these visitors were naturally from the communications media. When not on board during an outing, or following in the launch, the press tended to gather in the Latsi Hotel on the Poros waterfront, interviewing, gossiping, and waiting for something to turn up. It was all very reminiscent of Evelyn Waugh's *Scoop*: the trireme – it was August and the silly season – had been accorded the status of a modest African war. We had three British television crews, one Greek and one French; and correspondents and photographers from Italy, France, the USA and Bulgaria.

The place of honour that would once have belonged to *The Times* was now held by the BBC. Mike Purton from BBC East had been filming the story of the trireme since the earliest days, and had become part of the family, following us to Cambridge, Lowestoft, Coventry, Henley and Keratsini. He was now joined by a team for S4C, and another from the news programme with Kate Adey. Christian Tyler of the *Financial Times* and Christopher Dodd of the *Guardian* spent some time with us, and researched the background thoroughly. Barry James produced a learned article for the *International Herald-Tribune*, but *Time* magazine became the oarsmen's favourite when it credited us with a top speed of over 20 knots.

Returning to moorings had its tricky aspects. The mooring buoy was of necessity quite close to the quay wall, and in an angle formed by a projecting jetty. The approach was therefore restricted, and for the first few days the trierarch assumed personal command of this manœuvre. As his confidence in the crew increased, Lieutenant Papadas relaxed this, first by allowing the whole crew, rather than just the thranites, to row in, and finally on the second Saturday by letting our own *kubernetes*, Tim Shaw, take charge, which he did with his usual calm aplomb.

After each outing the officers, observers and leaders met together to discuss changes and improvements, and the crew dispersed to the beaches and tavernas.

Lieutenant Papadas, after thirty years in the Navy, had clearly at first been horrified by the noisy, irreverent and untidy crew (who had immediately christened him Captain Pugwash), but became mollified as he appreciated their dedication. In particular his admiration for John Coates was boundless (but then, so was everyone else's). Papadas had originally been asked to oversee the work at Tsakakos's yard, but after a couple of visits he had declined, thinking it impossible that the ship could ever be built there. Now, seeing how it had been done and recognizing that this was only because of John's consistent support, he became converted to the project. Relations also improved after a dinner at which the Captain was presented with a trireme T-shirt, which became his favourite off-duty wear. For their part the crew began to understand both the Captain's difficulties and his sterling personal qualities.

It was, however, true that the ship's construction left much to be desired. The spurt of activity that had got her finished just in time for the launching had been achieved at the expense of workmanship. The shelter deck was crudely put together, and the wearing parts of the propulsion system soon showed strain. The whole of the outrigger came away from its blocks, having been held in position only by the bolts; thole-pins, and thole-pin blocks broke; the leather thongs that should have held the blades to the thole pins frequently snapped and had to be replaced by rope loops. We never managed to paddle more than a score or so of strokes without something breaking, and became adept at effecting repairs while under way. Cries of 'Hammer!' would be heard passing down the deck, the defective oar would be pulled in, together with its opposite number on the other side, the repair done and the oars slipped back into the sea in time with the others.

As the trials proceeded the crew changed from a collection of enthusiastic individuals into a coherent unit, within which several smaller groups were identifiable. Some of these had been present from the start: a strong contingent from Oriel College, Oxford rowed together: a grey-haired group from Durham – the three oldest being Peter Burdess at fifty-nine and Brian Fenner and Bill McInnes at fifty-seven – gave strength to the thalamian level. There were several family groups: Richard Stanley-Baker had come from Hong Kong, his wife Joan from Melbourne and son Michael from England; no fewer than five Oxford Hassalls were present; John McDonnell, our counsel learned in the law, and his son Conrad rowed lustily; Peter McLeod brought two brothers, Jamie and David; John Brooks took part with his daughter Sylvie; there were three Baird sisters; and even, towards the end, a brace of Welshes.

Other groups either developed from their positioning in the ship, or found the slots that suited them. The bow thranites, men to port and women to starboard, who had an uninterrupted stroke but more resistance to overcome, were an outgoing lot, and thranites in general, perhaps, recalled that

Fig. 67 View of the crew in situ

they had been regarded as the cream of the crew in classical times – given for example, a special bonus before the Sicilian expedition. The thalamians certainly had the worst of it in their cramped quarters, where the smell of sweat seemed to settle and reside (and where we discovered the answer to the much-canvassed question of what served for heads in the trireme: a discreet plastic bag in the little space under the fo'c'sle).

A potentially serious matter was raised by an anonymous communication (but evidence suggested our QC) on the noticeboard, headed '200 BRITONS IN MASS CRIME' and pointing out that the trial crew and observers were rendering themselves liable to prosecution under the Foreign Enlistment Act of 1879, which makes it an offence punishable by up to two years' imprisonment for any man (or presumably woman) to place himself under

*Fig. 68 View of the light
upper deck*

the command of an officer of a foreign military power – a crime which was demonstrably being committed every time we set out with Lieutenant Papadas.

A possible defence was suggested by another legal brain:

'In R v Jennings the accused was charged under the 1879 Act for having served as a lancer in the troops of the Pasha of Izmir. Lord Austin of Brickwell stated that if the accused could produce evidence of 'critical insubordination', he would not come under the 1879 Act. Though his Lordship did not adequately define 'critical insubordination', he stated in no unclear terms that outperforming the foreign commanding officer in an alcoholic beverage consumption competition was an instance of critical insubordination recognized by law. Those of you interested in raising this particular defence, sign your names so we can arrange the details.

The correspondence was concluded by the black team challenging the captain to a beer race at any time, which, from my observation, might have been a near-run thing.

Not being anything more than the crudest of barge boat scullers, I was at first confused to find Mike Budd and the other rowing men referring not to 'port' and 'starboard' but 'bow' and 'stroke' (or at least I think they were: Mike never got the hang of 'port' and 'starboard' either). This reflected an uncertainty as to what the trireme actually was: far too big to be a boat like *Argo*, she is something that has not been seen for centuries – a rowing ship. Designed for the maximum speed and manœuvrability in action, she nevertheless had to be able to make long fast passages. Sail was never used in battle, the masts often being left in the dockyard since, as we discovered, the spars and ropes, even when lowered, made for a cluttered deck (fig. 68), which would have badly impeded fighting men.

We had, however, squeezed into the tight programme three short sailing tests under the direction of Owain Roberts (fig. 69) as sailing master. A schoolteacher from Anglesey, Owain is an experienced mariner who, meeting John Coates at a conference, had manifested an interest in discovering how the trireme sailed. As soon as Owain saw the trireme he detected an anomaly which had not appeared in the drawings and which had its roots in the peculiarly Tsakakos method of construction. In traditional sailing ships the masts are solidly based right on the keel itself, rising throughout all the decks of the vessel. If such a mast ever has to be removed a major operation is required, necessitating the use of sheer legs (often mounted on a superannuated hull, hence 'sheer hulk') to extract the mast rather as a tooth is drawn. Smaller boats, or those where masts often require to be lowered, as with Thames barges, have their masts mounted on deck. The bracket, which acts as a hinge and in which the mast is then fixed, is known as a tabernacle. Needless to say, since the tabernacle takes all of the compression strains of the mast, it needs to be a solid affair, strongly fixed. On a barge the tabernacle sits on a substructure of steel columns, which themselves are secured to the kelson. In a trireme the design and construction of a tabernacle needs even greater care, due to the peculiarities of its rig.

Usually the mast is also supported by stays – ropes that run from the

Fig. 69 Owain Roberts

mast to the deck along the centre line of the ship, and shrouds, which run from the mast to the sides of the vessel. Sometimes, however, the mast is completely unstayed, as in some modern designs; occasionally it is supported only by stays, without shrouds. It is clear from many pictures that this is what was done in ancient ships, and John Coates had accordingly designed a rig with only fore and aft stays.

This naturally placed even more importance on the secure fixing of the tabernacle, which had not only to withstand the compressive strains of the mast, but to do the work of the shrouds; it had been designed with these factors in mind. But the ship had come from the Tsakakos yard with a tabernacle so loose as to be potentially dangerous, and the danger had been exacerbated by another building error. Instead of being made from separate pieces of wood lashed together as designed (fig. 70), the main yard had been glued into a solid and immovable spar. What *should* have been

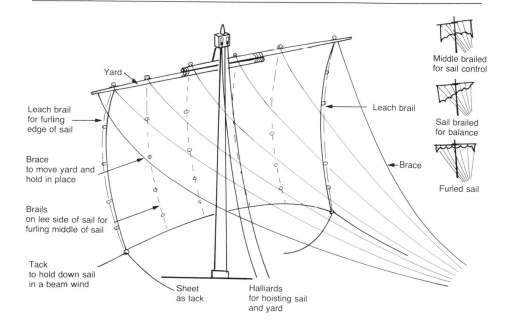

Yard

Leach brail
for furling
edge of sail

Brace
to move yard and
hold in place

Brails
on lee side of sail for
furling middle of sail

Tack
to hold down sail
in a beam wind

Sheet
as tack

Halliards
for hoisting sail
and yard

Leach brail

Brace

Middle brailed
for sail control

Sail brailed
for balance

Furled sail

done can be seen in the Kyrenia merchantman (fig. 29). Her firm shrouds were both situated aft of the mast, allowing sufficient space for the yard to be braced well round. And the yard itself was properly assembled in three pieces, lashed together. The flexibility thus given allowed some of the stresses generated by the sail to be absorbed by the yard, and had reportedly stood up to gale-force winds.

The massive and unyielding spar we had been landed with permitted no such latitude. Both its own weight and the propulsive energy of the sail were transmitted straight to the mast and Tsakakos's defective tabernacle. The Salamis dockyard, understandably worried for the safety of the mast, had therefore added a pair of shrouds on either side. Unfortunately, as well as being completely unhistoric these had been rigged in such a way as to make it impossible to raise the yard without loosening the foremost pair of shrouds, or to tack without slackening the leeward shroud. We were therefore faced with only being able to sail with a stern wind or one slightly on the beam.

Owain was understandably unhappy at this restriction, but having regard to the short time available for sail trials, it is doubtful whether any

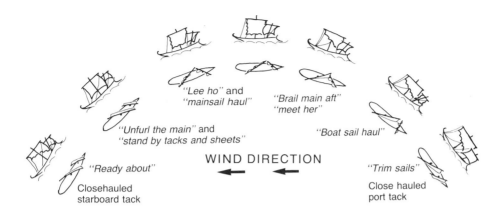

Fig. 70 The sails and rigging of the trireme (left)

Fig. 71 How a trireme would tack (above)

more could have been done. As befits a schoolmaster, Owain had prepared a training programme, with illustrations showing exactly how the sails were to be operated. If we had been able to tack the trireme, fig. 71 shows how it would have been done.

As it was, our first venture with the sails took place in the lightest of following winds; any motion of the ship was imperceptible, but in fact she glided forward at some 3 knots, her fine underwater lines offering little resistance. This was another historic moment, the first time a trireme had been seen sailing for at least 1,500 years. Obligingly, it took place against the most romantic of sunsets, with the mountains over Troizen making a magnificent backcloth (fig. 72).

We had a much better wind on the long day's outing, which had been meant to be the last day of the trials. This took place in the open sea north of Poros, and proved to be altogether more spectacular. The wind was nothing more than a respectable breeze, force 2–3, but the ship fairly steamed ahead under both sails, throwing up a fine bow wave around the ram, and logging 6 knots. The oarsmen, who were always on board in order to keep the ship's trim right, were mightily pleased at this, and thereafter

Fig. 72 The trireme under sail

were very keen to have at least the boat sail hoisted to help them on their way. Even this limited experience suffced to show that, in the right conditions, the trireme could really lift up her skirts and move, and that ancient oarsmen would have been quite as willing as our crew to accept the assistance of the wind. With the mainsail hoisted, rowing would have been practically impossible, but it seems likely that in light airs the boat sail might have been used as an auxiliary to the oars.

Brief though our tests were, Owain was enthusiastic about the potential of the trireme as a sailing ship, and anxious at a later date to have the opportunity of making further experiments, over a longer period, and with the original rig in place.

Since we had been able to sail, thanks to the impediment of the shrouds, only with a following wind, in which the ship stayed upright (she would lean over only with a wind coming from one side), we were not able to see how much water was shipped through the thalamian ports. Even with oars shipped (pulled into the ship) the spoons protruded for a yard or so, and these would probably themselves act as a barrier to any great quantity of water coming through. Certainly our thalamians betrayed no nervousness at sitting behind such large ports, so near the waterline, protected only by a leather screen. In spite of the limited time we had to test her under sail or in any sort of a sea, we felt confident that our trireme would do well enough in the right conditions.

The Thursday's programme centered around our only attempt at 'beaching' the ship: for the rest of the time we had worked from the quay. This operation, which was carried out every night and normally at midday, is portrayed on the Ruvo vase, and consists of backing the ship into shallow enough water to enable the crew to land. Lt Papadas had selected a convenient cove off the north coast of the island for the attempt. Being the first occasion on which a trireme had been beached for quite some time, we went about it gingerly enough, paddling to within a prudent distance from the shore and then warping her in from ropes secured to convenient rocks. Eventually – and this took some little while – she rode happily only a few feet from the beach, while the crew behaved almost exactly as they would have done in ancient times – they swam in the beautifully clear waters of the bay and ate their midday meal. Almost exactly, at any rate: we had the advantage of some attractive girls, and the disadvantage that the beach was inches deep in rubbish swept there by the northerly winds from the droppings of tourists in and around the Saronic Gulf.

9

Conclusions

WE had intended that the full day's outing on Thursday should mark the end of our sea trials, but the last-minute alterations had led to something of a contretemps. More than forty guests, all friends and supporters of the Trust, had arranged to come to Greece to see the trireme in action and to be present for the commissioning. They were, however, now arriving in Poros only on the Thursday night, and, unless we could extend the trials over Friday, they would not see anything of the ship's working.

All of the crew who were able to readily agreed to stay for the Friday particularly since this would give them a chance of proving the effectiveness of John Coates's design to a knowledgeable audience and of demonstrating their own ability to make the ship perform. Many of the earlier television films had been taken before the crew had developed their skills, but now they were full of confidence and anxious to show their ship off a bit.

The morning's outing took the form of a long paddle past the town of Poros, intended to give the townsfolk the opportunity of having a close look at the ship in action. It also gave an unexpected example of the major limitation of the trireme as a sea-going vessel – her susceptibility to weather. After rowing past the town into the open sea, we had to make a turn in order to paddle back. The head wind was no more than a strongish force 3, but was enough to kick up a modest chop which proved quite sufficient to cause some consternation during the turn up into the wind. Caught in the unexpected swell, some of the oarsmen missed their stroke and became momentarily entangled. Had this happened earlier in the trials, before the crew had acquired the knack of extricating themselves, it could have proved dangerous. In war a confused reaction to these circumstances could indeed be fatal, as was proved in at least one naval battle described by Thucydides, and quoted in *The Athenian Trireme* (page 70).

> As the breeze freshened, the ships which were already in a constricted space were beginning to fall into confusion from the simultaneous effect of the wind and of the smaller vessels, and ship was jostling ship and poles were being used to keep them apart. And as the seamen [i.e. the deck hands] were shouting and taking evasive action, and abusing each other, so that they were not listening out for the words of command or for the boatswains, and as the ill-trained oarsmen, being unable to recover their oars in the choppy water, made the ships unresponsive to the helm, at that precise moment Phormio gave the signal, and the Athenians, moving in to ram, first sank one of the flagships, and then went on with the intention of putting the rest of the ships out of action as they fell in their path.

This describes very precisely the likely behaviour of a badly trained crew, such as ours had been to start with but now proved to be no longer. They had by then already experienced milder forms of the same thing in the shape of washes from inconsiderate powerboats, and made a quick recovery, which would have saved the situation in that battle.

The evening passed more peaceably. The launch which had served as tender and rescue boat failed to turn up, but we continued to load all the visitors on to the ship's deck. There must have been sixty people on deck, twice as many as the trireme had been designed for, but she took the extra load gracefully.

Rowing with some benches empty, since some of the crew had already had to leave, the ship was pulled off down the straits. In spite of being overloaded and undermanned she never performed better. The blades met the water together, and pulled firmly in perfect unison as she glided into a romantic sunset for a sedate excursion around the harbour.

On her return, as she neared the quay under all oar, the crew started singing 'Jerusalem'. Though not, perhaps, immediately obvious as a rowing song, Parry's music and Blake's words, heard distantly over the calm sea, were ineffably moving. As they disembarked the crew was quieter than usual: something unique and valuable had come to an end: one young man sat on a bollard, sobbing openly.

It did not, of course, last very long, this unwonted outburst of sentiment. Within a very few minutes the whole lot were baying for Mike Budd to step ashore in order to receive the traditional farewell given to a successful cox. The prudent Budd, not much liking the idea of being hurled into the decidedly insanitary waters of Poros harbour, refused to leave the ship by way of the gangplank, but waited on deck for the enthusiasm to abate. When this showed no sign of happening, the Hellenic Navy, always prepared, secured his retreat by means of a rubber dinghy, and Mike made off towards the town, waving gracefully to his admirers.

This evasion was fruitless: less than ten minutes later a mob had dashed from the barracks, rooted out Mike from the bar a good 300 yards away where he had taken refuge, and carried him bodily back to the quayside for the now inevitable ducking. This appalling behaviour on a naval base would have caused horrified reactions from the authorities a few days earlier, but they had quickly come to terms with the rather different habits and customs of the English young. It spoke volumes for the authority of Lieutenant Papadas that not even the rashest Oxonian thought of ducking *him*: he received equally traditional but more respectful cheers.

That was not quite the end of the Poros trials. The crew's own celebration on the Friday was followed the next day by a dinner with the Mayor of Poros given by all the local travel agents, and which ended with energetic Greek dancing under the guidance of Stathis Alexopoulos, matched by English drinking songs led by Al Green and Graeme Fife.

Five years after our conversation over dinner in Westmorland, and twelve years after *The Times* correspondence, we now had sound facts to go on. At least the major points of the controversy could be settled.

The original argument had centred on two points: could a three-level oared ship, with oars of similar lengths, work in practice; and could the speeds under oar recorded in the fourth and fifth centuries BC be reproduced today? Around this had grown a separate debate as to how far the John Coates design was a faithful reconstruction of an ancient Athenian trireme.

On the first issue it can certainly be confirmed that a ship built as we conceived the Athenian trireme of the fifth century BC to have been, with three rows of oars all of similar length, and of dimensions that fitted inside the ship shed, could be made to perform very much as the historians had recorded. While this is not exactly the same as saying that John Coates's design is a replica of a fifth-century ship, those who disagree are going to

Fig. 73 Photograph of our trireme for comparison with the Lenormant relief:
see Fig. 13

have to build a better one if they wish to prove their point (fig 73). I would not encourage them to do so: not often can a friendly disputation have been settled in so expensive and arduous a fashion.

The results of the trials are still being analysed by Ian Whitehead but the preliminary figures speak for themselves. The ship could accelerate from standing start to 6 knots in 30 seconds. Another 30 seconds would send it off, at the same speed, in a 90° angle of turn. Several measured distances of 500 m were covered in 2.30 minutes or less, a speed of over 12 kph or $6\frac{1}{2}$ knots. The average speed over a longer distance was not unsatisfactory – 2 kilometres in 13 minutes, or 9 kph. The maximum speed recorded was just over 7 knots under oar, and 6 knots under sail with a beam wind of 15 kph.

These are already performances that would make the trireme a most formidable fighting ship, and they are certainly capable of considerable improvements, many of which may be identified. In the first place we had deliberately used heavy oars, in order that they should be able to stand up to the rough treatment that we knew they would receive. An experienced crew could be equipped with lighter oars made of spruce, thereby lessening the effort that would be needed to produce the same speed. It would indeed be worth having two sets of oars, heavier for training and lighter for performance. We did not experiment, either, with using only one steering oar, or even taking both from the water: these massive blades, if left in the sea, create considerable drag. These two improvements between them might alone result in an increase of up to 1 knot in speed.

Then, and this is a subjective observation, a ship which was more soundly constructed might engender a greater feeling of security, enabling oarsmen to exert more power. Certainly the frequent breakages reduced speed, and the wasted effort caused by ill-fitting oar thongs was very audible as oars crashed against tholes at every stroke.

These are, however, modest improvements compared to those that could be made with a different crew and more training. We had made no effort whatever to select our crew: we had simply accepted all volunteers, and ended up with all shapes and sizes. It was little short of a miracle, and reflects the greatest credit on our oars and coaches, that the crew performed so well. Indeed their very differences may have helped in the earlier stages; when all were experimenting in entirely new techniques it was perhaps useful that they had to learn these at the same time as fitting in one with another.

But there can hardly be any question that a crew chosen to harmonize in power and size must be able to perform appreciably better, although this might be even more visible in improved endurance than in maximum speeds. Stamina is, I am told, at its best when one is in the late twenties and thirties, and many of our most enthusiastic oars were still in their teens. The Durham veterans, pressing sixty, although they found the going tough, held out more easily than those of less than half their age.

The question of training looms even more importantly. The anonymous writer of 430 BC or thereabouts known as the Old Oligarch, or pseudo-Xenophon, recorded that:

The Athenians, because of their overseas possessions and the public offices they hold abroad, learn to use the oar as second nature, both themselves and their attendants. In fact when a man is often at sea he must of necessity take an oar himself and likewise his slave, and learn the language of the sea.

The majority are able to pull an oar when first they set foot aboard a warship, having had the preliminary training man and boy up to that moment.

206

Writing at about the same time Thucydides has Pericles say: 'The fact is that seapower is a matter of skill, like everything else, and it is not possible to get practice in the odd moment when the chance occurs, but it is a full-time occupation, leaving no moment for other things,' – as many University oarsmen have discovered while trying to fit some studies into a rowing life. And Thucydides, it will be recalled, was himself a trierarch, and knew what he was talking about.

In just over forty hours of training, which was what our devoted crew received, they had to start by rediscovering the basic skills before they could begin to practise them. The records that were set in the fifth century were established by men to whom oarsmanship was a 'full-time occupation', and who had received 'preliminary training, man and boy'. When this major allowance, by comparison with which such factors as the weight of the oars are negligible, is made, then the re-enactment of some of the ancient voyages becomes quite a feasible prospect.

We could now imagine what might be regarded as a 'long day', even in mid-August, two months after the solstice. A brisk start at 5.30 a.m. and a finishing time of 8.30 p.m. would enable everything to be done in daylight – 15 hours, which validates John Morrison's calculation (see page 69). This gives an average speed of some $7\frac{1}{2}$ knots, rather more than the maximum we had managed under oar but quite within the realms of possibility, given a balanced, properly trained crew. (And, quite possibly, a bit of help from the boat sail also.)

Various suggestions were made as to what would constitute an ideal crew. Mike Budd would like to see some West Country sea-oarsmen, who took part in the gig races, forming part of a crew; the Durham veterans suggested a combined veteran crew; Australian surf-boatmen might also be ideal. It is quite possible that an all-women's crew would do as well as, or better than, our mixed crew. Our women, who ranged in size from 6' (Lucy Baird from Newcastle) to some very slight girls, pulled well in all sections of the ship, and adapted to the new techniques more quickly than most of the men.

Whatever the composition of the crew, hard training is essential. After two weeks, at the height of the summer, many of our crew were tired, but we had still not managed to gear up performance to approach the optimum. At least three weeks, preferably with preliminary training using an enlarged mock-up, would be necessary, and at a rather cooler time of year. If this were to be done, we are confident that a strong crew would achieve much nearer classical times.

Fig. 74 The lethal ram, with traditional eye painted above

Although we might reasonably regard the old controversy as closed, its passing need not be too much regretted since we were able to start a few other hares which might run equally well.

In the first place, the speed and manoeuvrability of the trireme defined, for the first time, the performance that might have been expected of an early classical warship. Later warships, of which the best example is the Punic ship at Marsala, would never have been capable of matching them. That slow and unwieldy liburnian – if indeed that is what the Punic ship was – would have been a sitting duck for a trireme (fig. 74). John Coates has questioned whether the Marsala ship was ever intended as a fighting ship; but it is equally possible that the nature of naval warfare had changed radically in the intervening centuries, making weight and power the decisive factors.

While this is a matter for naval historians, some entirely new evidence stemmed from the behaviour of the crew. The success of the trials was due to the exemplary way in which the crew adapted. We had tended to assume that a crew was a complicated and rather tiresome necessity essential for the purpose of validating some theories. None of us realized how much we would be able to learn from observing the way in which 200 widely different people, united only through keenness for rowing and readiness for a little adventure, developed into a united and coherent body. The beauty of the ship, and the difficulty of discovering a new technique, formed them into a very unusual phenomenon: a team, without stars, but one in which any single member could bring about failure.

Modern sport is an affair of individuals or small groups, the largest probably being the crew of an ocean-racing yacht. Two hundred people working together is unprecedented in sporting terms. The armed forces and business bring people together in similar numbers, and expend much thought and effort into developing co-operation between them. But such units – a warship's crew, a rifle company, or a merchant bank – are made up of individuals each using a specific skill which contributes towards the success of the whole, some much more so than others.

The oarsmen of a trireme on the contrary all have one single task: to pull the blades. They must, however, do this in perfect unison, working one with another in what becomes an almost instinctive fashion. Any accident must immediately be remedied by those around. The analogies with an organism are tempting, and not unduly far-fetched. Watching from a helicopter, the trireme reminded John Morrison of some giant insect: the oarsmen have been described as moving in unison like a flock of seabirds. Our crew formed a team without parallel in modern times. (A good many enthusiasts left wanting to start the new sport of trireme racing, and full of proposals to build another in England. In the immediate future, however, we can content ourselves with having different crews attempt to better each other's times, as we hope to be able to do in 1988.)

More seriously, some new insights into the nature of ancient Greek society began to emerge from the experience of rowing together in the peculiarly intimate conditions of the trireme. We saw that doing so demands not only considerable skill but a capacity for tolerance and a mutual respect, which it is difficult to imagine existing other than in a democratic society.

Athenian democracy in the early fifth century was a relatively tender plant. The last of the tyrants had been banished only a few years previously. There were many still distrustful of handing over power to the mob, but the logic was inescapable: cavalry and heavy infantry, arms which required each man to provide his own expensive equipment, depended on wealthier citizens, and there were not enough prosperous Athenians, even with the support of their allies, to stand a chance against the overwhelming Persian power. Naval warfare alone offered the opportunity to meet the enemy on anything like equal terms, and the fleet demanded every man it could find. Themistocles requisitioned the services of foreigners living in Athens to supplement those of the citizens in order to secure the 40,000 men he needed to serve in the triremes.

At that time there was no question of using slaves to man the oar benches, and our experience showed how impossible this would have been. Anything less than total dedication and a willingness to work together as equals would be unacceptable. That fact was recognized by the most basic of all criteria, pay. Those fighting at Salamis do not appear to have been paid at all, but when rates of pay were recorded, they were the same for all hands – one drachma a day, irrespective of status.

After defeating the Persians Athens enjoyed the command of the seas for two generations before wasting her strength in fighting other Greeks. During that period competition for the services of skilled oarsmen increased. They were too valuable to be risked as fighting men except in the direst of emergencies, and bonuses were paid to secure the services of those most in demand – officers and thranites. Later in the century even slaves were allowed to row, but with the promise of freedom, which must have secured their hearty co-operation. As long as Athens needed a large fleet to expand and secure its supremacy it had to ensure a supply of sailors, and its sailors had to be citizens, and so Athens of necessity was a democracy with a wide franchise. Thus the practical requirements of managing a trireme were sufficient to underpin the world's first democratic experiment.

Physical factors of this sort are a great help in understanding the lives of our forebears. Using horse-drawn transport, or sailing working boats, or even simply walking long distances gives some idea of what life was like before steam came, but the trireme goes back a further couple of millennia. Our crew were experiencing exactly the same conditions as their predecessors, and probably reacting in very similar ways. Diverse, boisterous, irreverent, not too ready to accept discipline, needing to be handled properly, they were also dedicated to making their ship perform at her very best and smash whatever enemy might venture across their path.

If anyone should wish to have a flavour of authentic fifth-century Athens, he should try pulling an oar in our trireme.

There were those, then as now, who did not appreciate all aspects of democracy. The Old Oligarch, whom Peter Levi rather unkindly calls a 'bone-headed kind of conservative', had to acknowledge that the 'common people who serve in the trireme' brought the city of Athens her power, but characterized the masses as 'displaying extreme ignorance, indiscipline, and wickedness', people who had brought the pursuit of culture into disrepute 'because they realize that these accomplishments are beyond them'. At that time, before the Peloponnesian wars and the disastrous Sicilian expedition, Athens ruled a scattered empire by virtue of her command of the seas, and this command was due to the Athenian triremes and their crews.

A hundred years later, things had changed. Athens was but a member of the Macedonian Federation with a governor appointed by Alexander; and ships were no longer the fast triremes of Salamis, but bigger, slower vessels carrying quantities of troops. At that time Aristotle wrote in his *Politics* (VII, vi) that, in an ideal state:

> Large populations associated with a mob of seamen need not swell the membership of the state, of which they should form no part. The troops that are carried on board are freemen. They are in sovereign authority and have control over the crews

Aristotle clearly had no concept of what it was like to row in a fifth-century trireme, any more than we might today have of conditions in Nelson's navy. The idea of a crew like ours, prepared to give of their very best for a ship they loved, being subject to 'the sovereign authority' of infantrymen on deck, is absurd.

The Athenian trireme, like the longbow and the Kentucky rifle, was a weapon of democracy, in much the same way that cavalry has always been the arm of an aristocracy, and artillery (*ultima ratio regis*) that of a monarchy. Later galleys, larger and heavier, might well have been pulled by slaves (on a multi-banked oar, only the man furthest inboard needs to be skilled, since the others only add muscle), but the fast trireme needed just such an independent-minded, noisy, opinionated a crew as we had, quite unintentionally, provided. In this way an authentic aspect of Athenian life had been re-created, and not the least important aspect, either. Whatever interesting points emerge from future work on the ship – and we have as yet only developed the most elementary conclusions from a still-modest amount of evidence – our understanding of fifth-century Athens has been vividly clarified. And anything that adds to our appreciation of that remarkable period must be accounted something of an achievement – a not unsatisfactory outcome to a casual conversation after dinner.

Envoi

AFTER the departure of the 200 oarsmen and their supporters, Poros returned to its normal tranquil state. Those who were able to stay to form the nucleus of the commissioning crew started training in Piraeus. In this ten-day interval between the conclusion of the sea trials and the commissioning ceremony, at which our ship would cease to be simply 'the trireme' and be given her proper name (and presumably, since she would be officially a warship, an officially designated classification number, which could surely only be T1), discussions were held with the Hellenic Navy on possible future co-operation.

The task of co-ordinating the activities of the Navy and the Trireme Trust, previously the responsibility of Commodore Kolliniatis, now retired, had been taken over by Commodore Apostolis Vassiliades, a sagacious and understanding officer. He agreed that a re-enactment of the Mytilene dash, if that could be arranged, would be the most striking test of a crew's skill and stamina. Having been taught a good deal by our first crew, we felt that a picked international crew, including a significant American contingent, could be formed to attempt this in the summer of 1988, and we have started work accordingly.

The commissioning was intended to be a grander occasion than we had realized: for a week previously Athens was endowed with thousands of blue-and-white posters announcing the event, which was to take place in the new sports arena on the waterfront between Piraeus and Old Faliron, and the scene a few weeks earlier of Greece's triumph in the basketball international.

By a pleasant coincidence the US Navy had chosen the same week to

Fig. 75 The trireme under sail and oar

Fig. 76 The commissioning ceremony: Melina Mercouris hands Lieutenant Papadas the laurel wreath

pay a visit to Greece. This was announced as a courtesy visit, but, unusually and rather stuffily, the ships were anchored some way offshore rather than moored alongside in a harbour. From our point of view, however, the USS *Saratoga*, an aircraft carrier, and her attendant vessels formed an appropriate setting.

Wednesday 26 August was fine and hot; in the evening people turned up in great numbers (but not including Mr Papandreou, for whose benefit we were told the date had been altered). The faithful fifteen from the original crew were there, including all the Stanley-Bakers, Alistair Green, Graeme Fife and other stalwarts, smartly dressed and looking much tidier than they had in Poros in the white shirts, shorts and shoes that now formed the new crew's uniform.

Admiral Vassilis Kapoulos made a long speech in Greek and John Mor-

rison a shorter one in English. Several priests sang an impressive *Te Deum* and a prayer to St Nicholas, patron of sailors. Melina Mercouris, looking beautiful as ever, scattered olive oil, wine and rose petals on the sea, and hung a laurel wreath over the *aphlaston*, assisted by an embarrassed Lieutenant Papadas (fig. 76). The ceremony was a blend of ancient, medieval and modern that would have been impossible anywhere but in Greece.

At the final moment the blue draping over the stern was removed to reveal the name that had been chosen for the trireme. She was to be *Olympias*, not after that very unpleasant lady, the mother of Alexander the Great, but as a suggestion that it might soon be time to have another Greek Olympic Games. (Well, trireme-rowing would make a much more suitable Olympic sport than synchronized swimming!)

The well-drilled crew, neatly formed up in sixes, boarded at the double and set off precisely, if rather slowly, into the Saronic Gulf. As well as some 50,000 people who were on land to see her off, thousands of others had taken to the water. She was surrounded by small craft, with helicopters buzzing overhead, but all these were quite properly ignored as the trireme *Olympias* proceeded in a well-conducted fashion towards the *Saratoga*.

Her pre-arranged route took *Olympias* out into the Gulf, past the entrances to the ancient harbours of Piraeus and near to the aircraft carrier. While this was a unique opportunity for photographers and moralists to compare the advances that had been made in the art of naval destruction over 2,500 years, it might have proved inconvenient, since the water around the aircraft carrier was forbidden to any other vessel on grounds of security, upon pain of instant destruction. We hoped that the near approach of NATO's latest warship did not occasion undue nervousness on board the *Saratoga*, but all went well. *Olympias* stopped at what must have been a safe distance, hoisted her yards and sailed off, very elegantly, to what will be her permanent base at Faliron, alongside the cruiser *Averoff*.

APPENDIX 1 : THE CREW

Leigh Acason
John Aizlewood
Henry Alexander
Jeremy Allen
James Alston
Mathew Amies
Peter Askew
Kevin Aston
Neville Aston
Geoffrey Austin
Timothy Austin
Nicholas Badman
Amy Baird
Helen Baird
Lucy Baird
Fiona Baker
James Bamforth
Tim Beaver
Eeva Berglund
Sarah Binns
Toby Blake
Alison Blunt
Sharon Bowley
Peter Mark Brett
Paul Brindle
Stephen Brindle

Neil Brisley
Ronald Brooker
John Alan Brooks
Stephanie Brooks
Sylvie Brooks
Carolyn Brown
Keith Brown
Paul Brown-Kenyon
Erica Bruce
James Bruce
Martha Brundon
Peter Burdess
Adrian Burns
Douglas Busvine
Andrew Callard
Richard Charrington
Geoffrey Chatas
Barbara Chrisp
P. Clarke
Jonathan Cloke
Vanessa Collingridge
Diana Coop
Julian Cooper
Mathew Covill
Colin Cox
Erica Cox

A. Creswell
Ian Crompton
Richard Crooks
Tim Crow
Robert Czwarno
Robert Dangerfiled
Jan Edward Darasz
Catherine Davis
Paul Deards
Richard De Lacey
Guy Neville Deslandes
H. P. Dickerson
Sally Duckett
Bruce Eadie
Brian Easson
James Elvin
Fiona Esson
Hugh Evans
Brian Fenner
Peter Fielding
Graeme Fife
S. R. Fitch
Catriona Fox
Irene Fuller
Douglas Galbi
Caroline Gilruth

WILLIAM GREEN
JIM GREGORY
ELEANOR GREY
DOUGLAS GURR
BEN HALL
CHRIS HAMER
RUPERT HARE
TOBY HARNDEN
ANDREW HARRISON
EDWARD HASSALL
NICHOLAS HASSALL
OLIVER HASSALL
TOM HASSALL
LAURA HAWKSWORTH
STEVEN HIGGINS
ANDREW HILL
MAISIE HILL
NIGEL HILL-PAUL
BRIDGET HOLLAND
PHILIP HOLLOWS
TOM HOOPER
PATRICK HORTON
ADAM HOWARD
MARIA JOREVA
ALISON IRONSIDE-SMITH
ADRIAN JOHNSON
AVIN JOHNSON
BRIAN JOHNSON
ROSEMARY JOHNSON
ALASDHAIR JOHNSTON
MIKE JOLLY
DAVID JONES
ALEX KERSHAW
CHARLES KING
STEVE KING
JANE KIRBY
SIMON LINDSAY
OSMUND STUART LOW
NICHOLAS LOWCOCK
JEAN McCOLLISTER

ARCHIE McCONNEL
CONRAD McDONNELL
JOHN McDONNELL
RUPERT MACEY-DARE
JOHN MacGINNIS
WILLIAM McINNES
JAMES MACLEOD
DAVID MACLEOD
PETER MACLEOD
IAN McNAMARA
P.S. MACPHERSON
KEVIN McWILLIAMS
PAUL MALLET
WILLIAM MANNING
YANNIS MANUELIDES
PAUL MARKWICK
DOMINIC MARTIN
I. P. MAVROMMATIS
PHILIP METCALFE
ANDREW MILLER
DAVID MILLER
ALISON MILLS
HENRY MILNER
GRAHAM MORRELL
JAMES MORRIS
TED MOULDING
GEOFFREY MUGGRIDGE
HELEN NEWSAM
RICHARD NORTON
TREVOR NOTT
ERICA OTHEN
SOPHIE PAINTER
HAZEL PARKER
JULIA PARKES
JUDE PAYNE
MARK PAYNE
HUW PEACH
GREGORY PIPE
JAMES PIPE
CHRISTOPHER POLACK

FIONA POLACK
KONRAD POLLARD
GRAEME PROUDFOOT
JAMES RANKIN
PHILIP RAWLINS
MATTHEW RHODES
JASON RICHARDS
PAUL RICHARDS
PENELOPE RICHARDS
MARTIN RICHMOND
MATTHEW RIDGEWELL
SEAN RINGSTEAD
CHRIS ROBERTS
DEBORAH ROGERSON
JIM RONALDSON
ROBERT RONALDSON
ANDREW RUDDLE
MICHAEL SCHOLES
IAN SHARP
TIM SHAW
SEAN SINCLAIR
JOHN SNELL
JO SPREADBURY
COLIN SPRINGFELLOW
STEPHEN SPROWART
HENRY STANFORD
JOAN STANLEY-BAKER
MICHAEL STANLEY-BAKER
RICHARD STANLEY-BAKER
BRIGID SUTCLIFFE
SARAH TALBOT
BRUCE THOMPSON
PETER THOMPSON
ZARA THOMPSON
JAMES THOMSON
SIMON TIPLADY
THEODOR TROEV
PHILLIP TULLY
CARLINE TURNBULL
J. A. TURNBULL

STEPHEN WALTER	BEN WELSH	MICHAEL WIGSTON
MICHAEL WARD	JOHN WELSH	NICHOLA WILBERFORCE
CLARA WARDLE	SALLY WHITE	JUSTIN WILLIAMS
SHAN WAREING	RUPERT WHITE	MICHAEL WILMOT
VINCENT WARNER	EMILY WHITEHEAD	RICHARD WOODS
TIM WATSON	JOHN WHITING	TIM WRIGHT
ALLAN WATT	PETER WHITTALL	MIKE ZEIDLER
S. FORD WEISKITTEL	DAVID WIGG	

APPENDIX II: AN OARSMAN'S VIEW

An uneasy babble of voices up and down the boat. Nothing from the upper decks, and that will be the pattern from now on. Turns out they do a lot of screaming and shouting up there but all we get is the mind-boggling contradictions that arise out of that. Snorts and pings from the megaphone . . . the pulling master is showing his first-day nerves in his uneviable position – Mike Budd, a last-minute replacement for Boris Rankov, dumped in the deep end, all right. We begin to get the feeling that the whole thing has been stitched up with garden string and run by plastic gnomes; and, with the unthinking self-assurance of the ignorant, reckon that the sooner we get our blades in the water the sooner the whole business will be sorted out.

At last the order comes. 'Thranites only, backstops, are you ready? Row!' As we nose gingerly out into Poros bay, we begin to realize we've got a job on our hands. It's a long way from the swift flick through the water that we've been used to. It's like stirring a good mix of cement. And what will happen when the other oars start fighting for the same bit of sea? 'Herodotos he say' and all that moral *apparatus criticus* is not going to be much more use than a lighted match in a high wind.

The zygians and thalamians run their blades out – a fumble, since the thole straps aren't yet greased. (The ancient boats must have stunk of mutton fat.) Off we go. But where do we put the blades? And how? When? In the water and now, of course – but there are already two blades there . . . actually, feels like three from down here in the bilges. Four! Where did that one come from? A zygian in front – push off mate, stick to your own patch. Can't be *this* complicated. Worse than Greek irregular verbs. It's a conspiracy. It's like eighty people trying to knit one sweater at the same time with outsize needles; nine football teams chasing one ball; a platoon of soldiers passing gobbledygook messages in semaphore, if you look over the side at the blades flying about. Each set of three – thranite, zygian, thalamian – has to find water in a tight sweep, no more than a yard of space. The problems of a racing eight are multiplied ten times down each side of the boat. The oar-tips should form a mesh in the water so that the three blades act, near enough, as one. But in this period of trial and error, oars crack together, get hooked over each other as one poaches another's water, then crash down on a third in the effort to get clear. Any more of this and we'll all be nervous wrecks; call it trieritis. The important thing, it's said, is not to think about it; much on the line of the English general who rebuked a subordinate for asking him to elucidate a contradictory order: 'Don't ask questions,' he said, 'do what you're told.' Try not to *think* about it? This boat is cramful of undergraduates, graduates, researchers, retired academics and opinion-rich racing oarsmen. Tell a seagull to give up flying! You can almost hear people thinking about it above the splash of water and the thwack, clack and thump of wooden looms playing quarterstaff over the wine-dark sea. Glance at the ungainly twitching of blades as we clutch at rhythm and it's like a bizarre clockwork representation of an addled brain striving for logic and reasoned argument once more . . . an animated figment of chaos. For we *are* thinking about it, and will continue to think about it and talk about it in the bars and tavernas of Poros long after the rowing is done for the day. We are not yet giving our bodies time or chance to absorb the problem which is, must be, essentially one of rhythm. The ancient Spartans used to dance as part of their military training – you can see vestiges of this in the graceful if, to our eyes, absurd high-kicking drill of the Evzoni outside the old palace in Athens: foot shadow boxing, recommended by trainers of athletes in classical times; the original Python silly walk. The men in the tavernas don't dance only for the tourists; the better ones do it for themselves, and it's a long tradition. *And* it represents the heart rhythm – something we cold-climate northerners have to learn as a social skill. It's not natural to us.

So we chase this elusive rhythm (easy for the men who formed the choruses in ancient tragedy) through the stroke patterns we learned in racing boats. However, those are of little help now; the whole cycle is different. One stroke more or less in time and with minimal clashing of blades shows – like the first moment of riding a bike – that it *can* be done; but it gives a very different sensation from the sliding-seat motion we're used to. One of the Durham oarsmen recalls fixed-seat rowing before the war; unlike the rest of us he slips comfortably back into the old style – hip swing, long reach, and high rate – which formed the basis of the famous Jesus College method. Above all, though, we have to accept the need to start from the beginning; in a way, the absolute beginners are at less of a disadvantage than you might suppose – they aren't prey to fixed ideas of how it should be done like the rest of us know-alls.

The second outing, with each bank of oarsmen rowing in sections on their own, achieves more. We begin to build up the pattern, finding our own water, coaching instinct by watching each other more closely. There's a saying in the building trade: 'There are two ways of doing something – the short-cut way and the right way.' We've got two weeks to attempt what it took the ancient Greeks (and they were no slouches) six months of training on top of generations of experience to achieve. Plainly that's absurd. But then, you could say that designing and building an Athenian *trieres* in the face of practical difficulty and intellectual uncertainty was absurd in the first place. That's what makes the whole thing so attractive. Besides, if we acknowledge that all we can do is test feasibility – a series of exploratory experiments – then these sea trials, albeit brief, are valid. Rather like Johnson's disclaimer of Berkley's theory on materialism, you can't quarrel with the existence of this wooden boat because you can kick it. And if you then row it, proofs of other hypotheses begin to follow.

After a few outings the rhythm begins to come, as we settle down and get the feel of the boat. The thranites are in a position to coach the other two layers, because they alone have a view of the water. In the old days the process would have been reversed: thranites were then the new boys and would have had to learn from the rest. It doesn't take long for us to go back to that, thranites taking time and length of swing from the oarsmen below. When all's said and done you can only row a boat one way, the efficient way, and if the *trieres* represents an extreme of design the betting must be that she also demands an extreme of efficiency to propel her, the oars 'beating the salt water into a froth at a single stroke following the bosun's chant', as Aeschylus puts it, describing the Greek fleet rowing out across the headland into the narrow Salamis channel opposite Perama in 480 BC.

We have a bosun's chant too; but it's all very Henley and Oxbridge and useless. On these blades there is no catch and finish, no gather through the recovery, no roll of the wrists at the turn. The oars, geared 3:1 (as compared to the usual 2:1) are heavy and cumbersome – harder work out of the water than in it. Also, we're pulling against a stretchy leather strap holding the loom against the thole-pin. Ther's some debate as to whether the loom should pull against the pin instead. Modern Mediterranean practice has dictated our arrangement, but I'd venture to say that rowing would be more efficient the other way round. In fact we tried this – turning in our seats to row the boat backwards instead of pushing at the oars to back her down, and the ease of the pull was markedly greater. Whatever the answer to the thole-strap/pin riddle is, it affects the movement of the blade: speed through the water is about the same as speed through the air and the ancient cry, *o-opop o-opop*, calls the rhythm exactly. It's not just romantic quest for authenticity, either: why should you not expect an ancient boat to respond best to the old system?

The debate over rating continues: we have no clear evidence to cover that. Some argue for a longer stroke, others for a higher strike. However, because of a quirk in the ship's construction, the thalamians in the stern are fractionally more closely confined by the fore and aft beams than in the bow sections. Their shorter stroke performance determines the reach down the whole boat. Nor can we say, with certainty, whether high strike rates (up to 44; and John Coates suggests that 50 ought to be possible) develop higher speeds. There remain, too, many inponderables; not least the fact that our crew is not uniformly strong, fit or matched in size. My instinct is for a high rate, especially since all but four or six blades must permanently row in moving water. I'm not impressed, either by the theory that we should try to clear our puddles in a series of *fahrtlek* bursts. The most obvious analogy is that of a hoop or wheel bowling along, tapped with a stick or the heel of a hand to maintain momentum. The more frequent the taps, the quicker it shifts. And in the *trieres*, built to turn and accelerate to full speed, speed comes from the technique of the racing start; short strokes at very high rate. And you can't lengthen: there *is* only one efficient length.

No question, either, that the sound of her at a fast rate of strike is stirring: oars smacking the thole-pins like so many spear-butts on hard ground, blades threshing the sea, the hiss of water along the hull. We get the sense of that as we go into a short piece of flat-out rowing. The ancients talked of the oar-banks beating like wings; of the *trieres* as a bird of prey, say the shearwater, waiting to swoop on its victim. Evocative stuff; a fearsome sight and, by association, sound. I have to confess, too, that every time we row out it's the Battle of Salamis again; and every time my admiration for the Greeks who rowed that fleet under Themistocles increases. How did they do it?

The serious business of the sea trials continues: speed tests (though we seem unable to raise much above 7 to 8 knots), long rows – a stint of one hour forty minutes one day. Surprisingly, it was not exhausting; in fact, as the swing and rhythm bore into our muscles, the work got easier. I still can't imagine myself pulling this heavy-loomed oar a whole day, mind, even with intermittent rests and an ancient Olympian training diet of dried figs and feta cheese – they swore by that, the fit hard men of Greece. Perhaps for the shorter-limbed, barrel-chested farmers and fishermen of fifth-century Greece a twelve-hour day toiling at the oar, as at plough and nets, was nothing exceptional.

While we are disappointed with the comparatively low speed, our turning-tests prove dramatic and exciting. A simple turn under rudder power, with the whole crew pulling, is smooth and gradual. The stern does not skid, either, But the *pièce de résistance* is a full-tilt swerve, where the boat gathers speed, the helmsman shoves the rudder blades hard down, and one side of rowers takes the boat on, the other side resting. The boat runs through 180 degrees about one-and-a-half times its length, taking not much more than a minute to complete the manoeuvre. It leaves a smooth, hook-shaped scar in its wake as evidence. Spectacular, if hard work for the oarsmen pulling! John Coates is delighted *and* surprised. We have the first real measure of the *trieres'* stunning agility that sent her twisting and turning in the seas with astonishing speed, like a Spitfire in the air. Ian Whitehead and I discussed this and we are convinced that while the *trieres* battles may have started as the confrontation of one massed fleet with another – just as the squadrons of allied and German fighter planes squared up over Kent in 1940 – once contact was made it must have been every craft for herself.

GRAEME FIFE

Bibliography

The prime source of information for anyone who would like to take the matter further is *The Athenian Trireme* by J.S. Morrison and J.F. Coates (Cambridge, 1986). Most of the original literary evidence is given in *Greek Oared Ships* by J.S. Morrison and R.T.Williams (Cambridge, 1968). Other books and articles of major interest are *Ships and Seamanship in the Ancient World* by Lionel Casson (Princeton, USA, 1971); *Trees and Timber in the Ancient World* by R. Meiggs (Oxford, 1983), *Ancient Ships* by Cecil Torr (Cambridge, 1984, reprinted in the Argonaut Library of Antiquities, Chicago, 1964); 'The Greek Warship' by Dr W.W. Tarn (*Journal of Hellenic Studies* 25, 1905); *The Greek Trireme of the Fifth Century BC*, ed. J.F. Coates and Sean McGrail (discussion of a projected reconstruction at the National Maritime Museum, Greenwich, 1984).

The translations are largely those to be found in those works, except for the Aristotle which is the Sinclair & Saunders Penguin version (London, 1981), and the Aeschylus, for which nobody can be blamed but myself.

One interesting and easily overlooked English parallel to the trireme research is the work done on the Newcastle galley, an account of which by W.R.G. Whiting is given in *Archaeologica Aeliana* (Newcastle, 1936).

INDEX

Numbers in *italics* refer to illustrations